Wild Goose Qigong
1st 64 Movements

Michael Tse

Tse Qigong Centre
Altrincham, England

Michael Tse
ISBN 1-903443-01-6
ISBN 978-1-903443-01-6

Published by:

Tse Qigong Centre
PO Box 59
Altrincham WA15 8FS
Tel. 0845 838 2285
Tel. 0161 929 4485

www.tseqigongcentre.com
www.qimagazine.com

First Edition: 2000
Second Edition: 2001
Third Edition: 2005
Fourth Edition: 2008

Chinese Calligraphy by Michael Tse

Dedication

I would like to dedicate this book to my Sifu, Grandmaster Yang Meijun. Without her I would not have this profound skill to share with all of you.

Michael Tse

Thanks to:

Darryl Moy for his many hours of design work and extraordinary patience in adding further illustrations and corrections during the editing process.

Thanks also to the following people who have proof read, typed or otherwise helped or made comments on the book:
(listed alphabetically)

Mike Baker
Jerry Apperson
Richard Daab
Vera Externest
John Hayes
Adah Masaoka
Sarah Moy
Jane Pollard
Mike Stenson
Dai Souk
Jessica Tse
Lawrence Tse
Michelle Tse
Adam Wallace

Contents

Foreword

Grandmaster Yang Meijun

If you could live to be 100 years of age and still be healthy, would you be happy? Of course, most people would answer, yes, no doubt about it. It is becoming more common for people to live longer, and today there are more people who are living to eighty or even ninety years old. Unfortunately, very few of them are healthy. Often they will have difficulty walking, not be able to enjoy their food and some may not even remember their names or the names of their children.

Once I had a next door neighbour who was more than ninety years old. One year she had an operation which left her feeling weak and dizzy and taking medicine all the time. Sometimes the medicine made her feel ill and so it took her a long time to recover. So old age is something many people can reach, but to live long and stay healthy is not so common. This is really high level skill and this high level could be said to describe my Qigong teacher, the late Grandmaster Yang Meijun, she lived to be 104 years old and she still did her practise and meditation till the end.

She was still active, still healthy and saw many people every day. She used her Qigong skill to help heal sick people who came to her from all over China, even Hong Kong and America. She was so special that she was named the Honorary Director of the Chinese Qigong Scientific Research Association as well as Consultant to both the Beijing Qigong Research Association and the Wudang Boxing Research Association. Grandmaster Yang was also the President of the Dayan Qigong Association.

Dayan Qigong (which means Great Wild Goose Qigong) is the skill which was passed to her by her grandfather when she was only thirteen years old. This particular Qigong system, called Kunlun Dayan Qigong, is over 1,800 years old. This skill originated in the Kunlun Mountain range in China and was initially developed by the Daoist priests who lived there but also was influenced by Si Dao An (311 to 385), a famous Buddhist monk of the Jin Dynasty.

On the mountain, there were many wild geese who also made it their home. By observing these beautiful birds and imitating their movements, (including, fluttering, swooping and spreading the wings), the monks found that they could heal illness, improve flexibility and help prolong life. Dayan Qigong is a very pure skill, having been secretly passed on from only one person to another when the practitioner reached seventy years of age.

Grandmaster Yang's Qigong skill was very special. She could transmit Qi (energy) to make you feel warm and make your body tremble in order to help release negative Qi. She could even cool down your body so that it felt cold. She could see the colour of your Qi (aura) and diagnose your illness just by looking at you or by placing her hands on you. She was even able to transmit her energy with five different kinds of flower fragrances: - jasmine, sandalwood, orchid, tree peony and mace.

This is a special skill belonging to the Dayan system. Each smell relates to a different internal organ. A person needs to be healthy in order to transmit these fragrances though. If the person is not healthy, then the smell will be unpleasant, even rotten.

Her skill was so unique and special that she was not only recognised and honoured numerous times by the Chinese government but also around the world.

Her book on Wild Goose Qigong (now out of circulation) has been translated

into many languages and her teachings have now spread. Just like a wild goose her skill has migrated to all parts of the world, including Hong Kong, Japan, Taiwan, New Zealand, Australia, Europe and North America. It has helped many people suffering from all kinds of illness, including heart problems, asthma, arthritis and poor circulation. Even cancer sufferers have benefited. All because Dayan Qigong works on clearing the negative (or sick) energy from the body, balancing Qi and blood and gathering fresh (positive) Qi from nature

Michael Tse
teaching Wild
Goose
Instructors

to make the body healthy and strong.

Grandmaster Yang was very healthy and she possessed strong Qi right up until her passing. In fact, her skin was soft like silk and her voice still retained a powerful energy.

When my students met her, they were all very shy because they could feel both her spirit and Qi were very powerful. One of the students was very nervous because he was afraid that she might see something about him that he did not want others to know by using her Sky Eye skill. Dayan Qigong skill is one of the top ten healthy Qigong styles recognised and promoted by the Chinese government.

Its long history has proven itself and today we are lucky to be able to have such ready access to this profound and special Qigong system. Until the 1980's, the Kunlun Dayan Qigong system was still a closely guarded secret.

In the following pages, I will relate her story which she told me over the many years that I studied with her. Each time I visited her, she had more stories and ideas on Qigong, Daoism and Buddhism to share with me.

There are too many to include here, so I will start with her history and then in my next books (Wild Goose 2nd 64 Movements Part I & II), I will share some more stories with you, including some of the higher level principles of the Wild Goose Qigong skill. I have greatly benefited from my Qigong studies with Sifu (teacher) and want others to have this same opportunity.

As always, I tell people that it is best to have a teacher to guide and teach you, particularly with such a profound skill as Wild Goose Qigong. It is very difficult to learn from

Grandmaster Yang Meijun and Michael Tse practising Dayan Sword

either a video or book and it is best to use them as a reference tool rather than learning from them entirely. However, I know that not everyone can attend a class, so I have tried to make the explanation of the movements as simple as possible. However, if you want to learn the skill properly, I recommend that you study with properly authorised Wild Goose Qigong instructor.

My teacher, Grandmaster Yang Meijun, decided to open the skill so people could benefit for their health. However, she was careful whom she chose to be teachers and has only authorised a very few to spread her skill overseas. At one time, I knew that Grandmaster Yang was very upset when she heard that some people were claiming to be her close students and using her name only to make money for themselves.

Without her, none of us would have this skill. So we should all respect her skill and study properly. I respect the skill that my teacher taught me and I do not want to see it spoiled by someone learning a little bit and then going out to teach. This is disrespectful to the teacher and their skill. I have studied Dayan Qigong for many years. It is an amazing skill which you are continually rediscovering. I myself did not teach until my teacher told me I was ready and allowed me to begin teaching in 1988.

Sometimes it is not the fault of the student but the teacher. I have seen videos and books on Wild Goose Qigong in which the movements were not correct. I know that a person following these movements can have problems. If you are studying Wild Goose Qigong under an instructor, you should find out whether that person is authorised to teach and understand the skill. You should also ask yourself if the instructor is healthy and what is their lineage, i.e. who they learned from and who their teacher learned from and whether they have been qualified to teach this form. If someone teaches without the permission of the teacher it is equal to stealing the skill. My own students must study with me for three years before they are nominated to become instructors and then must go back at least every other year to polish and retest their forms. In this way the skill not only survives but gets better.

For details of authorised instructors of the Tse Qigong Centre, you can visit our website or telephone us at one of the numbers given at the end of the book.

The history of a martial art or Qigong system is very important in Chinese culture. We consider our teacher to be like our father and call them Sifu, which means teaching father, even if they are a lady. Just as you called your school teacher "Sir" or "Miss" when you were young as a way of respect, we do not call our teachers by their first names. We always respect and take care of our teachers, even if there are times when we do not always agree with them.

I am lucky to have many good students who appreciate the skill I teach them and also respect the Chinese culture from which that skill originated. I know that if you understand more about the background of something or why it works and its benefits, then you will appreciate it more. That is why I have shared with you my teacher's story and also some comments of people who have benefited from their practice of Dayan Qigong.

This is the second time that these movements have been printed. The first was in my magazine, Qi Magazine, over a period of two years. At the request of my students and others, I share with you here the 1st 64 movements of Dayan (Wild Goose) Qigong. These have been revised and some additional illustrations added to help make the movements more clear. The descriptions have also been edited to make the movements easier to understand.

This book is now in its third printing and it has been 'polished' even more. If anyone sees any errors, I hope that you will let us know so that we can continue to improve and get better.

I hope you will enjoy this book and that we can join together again in the future for the 2nd 64 movements of Wild Goose Qigong and some of the other Dayan system forms, like Plum Blossom Gong and Jade Pillar Gong.

Good health and practice to you all.

Michael Tse

Chapter 1

Grandmaster Yang Meijun
27th Generation Inheritor of Dayan Qigong

Grandmaster Yang
as a Young Child

Looking at Grandmaster Yang, you would be surprised to find that she led a very dramatic life. She was very tiny and weighed less than eighty pounds. Yet when she spoke, her voice was full of energy and her strong spirit was obvious. She was born during the Qing Dynasty in 1898, on the 5th day of the 8th month. This was during the time when all the men had to wear their hair in queues or be considered traitors against the government. At the time there was still an Emperor who controlled the country and people had to do what the ruler said. At that time, the government said that all the men had to shave the front part of their head as well as keeping a long tail at the back. The saying at the time was, "Keep your hair and lose your head or lose your hair and keep your head".

Little Meijun's family was very poor and her father had to work by pulling a rickshaw, transporting people from place to place. It was very hard work and did not pay that well. Like most families in China at that time, it was not just parents and children all living together, it was the extended family as well. Her grandfather, Yang De Shan, had lived with her family for as long as she could remember. He was a tall man and she remembers that he usually wore the same clothes no matter what the season. Even though the winters in this part of China were very cold, her grandfather never wore much clothing, just something loose, nothing more than a light padded jacket. Despite this, he never seemed to get ill or catch any colds.

One evening when Little Meijun (which means Plum Blossom) was thirteen years old, her grandfather took her to a place called a "spiritual room". Inside the room, he lit some joss sticks and told her to kneel down and worship Buddha three times. Of course, she was curious as to why they were here and what was going to happen, but she did as she was told and did not ask anything. Her grandfather looked very serious as he watched her. Her grandfather then said, "Today, whatever we do, we are responsible to the Buddha. From now on you will follow me to study the Dao (a philosophy or school of thought which follows nature and the idea of cause and effect) and Qigong. Whatever you learn from me, you must keep secret. You are not allowed to reveal what I show you to any other person until you have reached the age of seventy." Although she was a little bit frightened inside and seventy seemed like a lifetime away, she nodded her head yes. She had always respected her grandfather and she listened to him. She thought to herself that no matter what he taught her, she would always listen and obey him.

White Pagoda Temple

In the hushed presence of the room, he continued to talk to her gently. "When I was a teenager, while I was in Sichuan I met a Daoist monk whom I came to know well. Eventually I studied under him. He was from the Kunlun Mountains and he taught me a special Qigong skill that had been passed to him by his teacher. He taught me many things, not only Qigong. He also taught me martial arts and how to heal illnesses. These things have only been passed down from the teacher to a specially chosen student. It has never been taught to the outside, only passed down inside his family. I was the first student from outside the family to learn."

"It was my thought that I should pass this skill to your father but he is already over fifty years old, and it would be difficult for him to learn my skill. I am getting older as well, and I need to teach someone otherwise these precious skills could be lost. You are the only person suited for this skill as you are young, and you have the time to learn. Tomorrow, we will visit a special temple and perform the ceremony which will make you my student."

The next day they set off before dawn. There were not many people about as they travelled to a place called the White Pagoda Temple. You can still see this temple today in Beijing's Beihai Park which is north of the Forbidden City. When you walk through the park, it is like a white sun, hanging above the trees and lake with its floating green lotus leaves. They had to climb several steps to get to the pagoda. It was late summer and it was very warm. When they reached the statue of Guan Yin Bodhisatva (Bodhisatva with the female image and Buddhist goddess of mercy), her grandfather instructed her to kneel and worship and to swear a special oath.

He then said to her, "You are the 27th generation inheritor of the Kunlun Dayan Qigong system", and he then took something from the bag which he was holding. Then he opened his hand and on his palm lay eight copper wild geese. Each of them was caught in some action of movement:- one drinking water, one flying away, one stretching its wings, one scratching its legs. Little Meijun thought perhaps they were trinkets for her to play with, but instead, her grandfather explained that these were some of the special wild goose movements that were in the Qigong forms that she was to learn, like Dayan Gong, Dayan Palm and Dayan Fist.

He said to her, "You must follow these movements to do them properly. I will teach you all these movements but you must withstand the difficulty and continue practising no matter what. One day you will fly away like a wild goose to get the Dao." Although she did not fully understand what her grandfather was saying, she knew it was something important, something that would change her life. She decided that she would do her best to overcome any problems that she met in her life so that she could keep her promise to her grandfather and Guan Yin Bodhisatva.

After the ceremony, they left the temple and she felt different inside. She was quieter than usual as she thought about that had happened, so she was very startled and scared when something with sharp claws grabbed at her as they passed through one of the gates. It turned out to be a wild monkey. Although very small, this kind of Chinese monkey can be ferocious. Suddenly, her grandfather was at her side and he lifted up his arm and pointed two fingers at the monkey's head. Within a second, the monkey's face contorted, as if it was in extreme pain, and then it ran away screaming.

She was very surprised at what her grandfather had just done and she said to him innocently, "I want to learn that skill, grandpa, so that nobody can attack me. I did not know you had that skill." Her grandfather looked down on his little grand-daughter and said kindly, "This skill I will teach you, along with many others, but it is not for hurting people. It is only for your protection. This skill can also make you live longer and healthier and can also help you heal other people as well." As they travelled back home, he continued talking, teaching her what was to be the first of her many lessons in Qigong. He told her that "Qi is the leader of the blood. When I pointed at the monkey's acupuncture point, the Qi stopped flowing and no blood could flow through that area, so he felt pain."

When they returned home, Little Meijun moved her things to live next door to her grandfather's room, not letting her parents know she was going to study with him. She said instead that she liked to spend more time with her grandfather and would help to take care of him. Everyone was so busy with their own things and trying to survive, that they did not bother. That night at 3:00am a hand on her shoulder woke her. It was her grandfather and he motioned for her to follow him outside into the darkness. Once outside, he said to her, this is the right time to practise. Nobody will disturb us."

From then on, she woke at three o'clock and practised until five o'clock every morning. She was taught things from the basic techniques of Qigong to learning the acupuncture points and principles of Qigong. She also learned about Daoism. Little Meijun listened to all her grandfather said and followed all he taught. For the first few days, her whole body ached and sometimes she felt a bit tired, but as each day passed, she felt herself getting stronger and stronger. In the beginning it was difficult to wake up in the middle of the night. Soon, however, she got used to it and it became a habit she kept all her life.

She began learning the 1st 64 movements of Dayan (Wild Goose) Qigong which is the basis of the Kunlun Dayan System. In this form, she began to copy the movements of the wild goose:- fluttering, swooping, spreading the wings. As she learned, her grandfather would check her movements strictly. Sometimes he would make her repeat what he taught her over and over again, only teaching her something new from time to time. So although she was learning things slowly, in this way he could be sure that she was learning the skill properly. He wanted to make sure that she picked up the principle behind the movements, not just imitating his movements. After many months had passed, she finished the 1st 64 movements of the Dayan Gong and began learning the 2nd 64 movements. She proved to be a clever student and this made her grandfather happy. He had found a suitable inheritor for his high level Qigong and so his heart was happy.

One night she asked him, "Why do we practise late at night and not in the day time?" He asked her a question back instead. "Do you know why the Morning Glory flower blooms at four o'clock in the morning and why the Peony smiles at seven and Tuberose releases its fragrance at eight?" When she shook her head, he continued, "From three to five in the morning is known as the 'Yin' hour." (The Chinese day is divided into twelve segments, each lasting two hours. Each segment relates to a particular channel and is good for certain organs. This is one of these times.) "It is during this time the Qi is strong in the lung channel. This a good time to practise because your Qi will be stronger."

Even though she was young, little Meijun learned quickly. She found learning about Qigong principles together with Chinese medicine was very interesting. Time had gone by very quickly. She completed Dayan Qigong 1st and 2nd 64. She even learned the higher level forms, like Dayan Palm, Triple Crossing Spiral Gong, Dayan Fist, Twining Hands Bagua, Sun Gong, Moon Gong, 28 Constellation Gong, Sky Eye Gong and many other high level Qigong skills.

Her practice continued with her grandfather, and during that time she noticed that on the first and fifteenth day of each lunar month her grandfather wanted to practise harder than usual. When she asked him why he said, "On these days the moon is full and is also closer than usual. Therefore we can gather more energy on these days."

Once her grandfather asked her a question to see how much she understood. He said, "Do you know why in the forms we begin movement on the right side first?" She pretended it was nothing serious and answered, "The left side of the body controls the Qi. The right side controls the blood. Blood runs slower than Qi, so we have more movements on the right side than the left. This stimulates the blood more and so we can then get balance in the body. Am I right, Sifu Grandpa?" and she looked at him with cunning eyes hoping to receive a reward. This made him very proud of his granddaughter.

A rickshaw puller

After many years of practice, one day she found herself very light, and she found that without even trying she could jump onto walls and even onto the roof of her house with ease. She was like a wild goose flying away. With her many years of hard training, she really tasted the benefits of Qigong. Her body was healthy and strong and sometimes she did not feel hungry, so there was no need to eat. Often just three or four hours of sleep a night was enough for her. Her grandfather was satisfied that she had learnt his skill and not long after he passed away. A few years after this, her mother also passed away and so all that remained of her family was her father and herself, but even this was not to last long.

One evening her father was transporting a Japanese man by rickshaw. Upon arriving at the destination, he asked for the fare but the Japanese man was drunk and refused to pay him the money. During the argument that followed the Japanese man pulled out a knife and stabbed her father, killing him. This greatly saddened Yang Meijun and she felt upset and lonely. She did not know what to do as she had lost her grandfather, mother and father and was now alone. She was all that was left of her immediate family.

Turning Sorrow Into Joy

At the time her father was killed, things were becoming very bad in Beijing. It was the time of the Japanese invasion and much of China was under attack. It was common to see Chinese civilians being insulted and abused and as time went on, things grew even worse. This made Yang Meijun very angry towards the Japanese, but there was little she could do, although someday she hoped she would be able have her revenge. Despite her sadness at her father's death and anger towards the Japanese, she kept her daily habit of her secret practice and slowly this helped heal her heart and make her more balanced. As she practised, she remembered one of the lessons that her grandfather had taught her about the emotions. He had said,

"Anger will damage the liver"
"Over-joy will damage the heart"
"Grief will damage the lungs"
"Worry will damage the spleen"
"Fear will damage the kidneys."

Meijun decided that it was time to move on and she remembered that she had an aunt living in the Gan Su County which is in northeast China, a place very far from Beijing. She left Beijing to find her aunt, hoping to change her situation and her fortune. However, when she arrived at Gan Su, she received the bad news that her aunt no longer lived there. By then she was tired and all alone. She did not know where to go or who she could rely upon in those desperate times. She had lost her direction and now felt lonelier than she had ever felt in her whole life.

However, she did not stay sad for long. She was a strong and spirited young woman who was also very clever. She noticed that the main trade in Gan Su was salt trading. In those days, however, they only employed men as the work was hard and also dangerous. She said to herself, "I have to find a way to survive," and so she disguised herself as a boy and joined the salt traders. At this time there was little order in society and there were many gangsters, especially in the salt trade. Those who controlled the salt made a lot of money.

Although it was physically very hard work, she found that she could cope as well as the men because of her many years of Qigong practice. She kept mostly to herself but there was one gentleman with whom she slowly became friends. His name was Chen Guo An, and he treated her very well even though he did not know that she was a girl. He was a man of good character and over time they built up a very good relationship. Then one day, he did not show up for work. Meijun did not think anything of this until he did not show up the next day or the next. She began to worry about her friend.

Maybe it was coincidence or maybe it was fate, but that evening she decided to go to an opera that was playing locally. Chinese opera is an integral part of the lives of even the very poor. It was good entertainment and helped people forget about the bad times around them. As she watched the opera, she noticed someone on stage who looked very familiar. Looking closer,

A Chinese Opera Performance

she realised that it was her friend, Chen Guo An. After the opera finished, she went to see him. He was very happy to see her, so much so that he invited her to come work with him in the opera. Even though the work was very simple, she agreed. She did not want to lose contact with Chen who had become her friend and family.

After some time, she found she that she no longer wanted to disguise herself as a boy. Slowly her female character started to show and she began to behave like a lady again. Chen Guo An was very pleased to discover his best friend was a girl. Their relationship changed and from best friends they fell in love. Very soon they married and started a family. One year later, they had their first child, a baby boy, and were a happy family.

One night around midnight, Chen Guo An awoke to find his wife missing. He was very worried when he could not find her anywhere inside the house and went outside to look. Suddenly he saw a shadow on the roof. The shadow moved very quickly, sometimes jumping up and down, like a bird. As he got closer his fear grew stronger, but then he realised it was his wife, Yang Meijun. Her skill and movements greatly impressed him and he asked how she had come to learn such a skill. He also wondered why she had not told him about it.

Yang Meijun, realising that her husband had discovered her secret, said, "This is my family's Qigong skill and I made a promise many years ago not to reveal it. That is why I did not let you know. Probably it is fate that you have now found out about my skill. This is good, so if anything should happen in the future you will not have to worry about me or our son." After that night Chen Guo An got used to her skill and treated it as normal.

Wartime

Around this time, the Japanese invasion of China was becoming more serious. They had conquered many provinces and the Second World War was just starting in Europe. Yang Meijun and her husband joined with volunteers who were banding together to help defend against the Japanese invaders. Often this meant travelling throughout the countryside. During these times she had the opportunity to meet many high level Daoist and Buddhist monks and nuns. They gave her a lot of help with her Dayan Qigong.

One Daoist told her of the principles of acupuncture points and channels. He said, "Your body is like the universe. There are many orbits and tracks crossing it. These orbits are our acupuncture channels. They bring Qi to different areas to balance the body and make the internal organs strong. This makes the body warm and function well. When we feel pain, stiffness or illness, it means the channel is blocked and needs to be smoothed. The acupuncture points are like the planets spread out over the body. These allow the Qi to enter, pass through and leave the body. If one point is blocked, this affects the whole system and illness will occur." This valuable knowledge helped her in the future when she developed her skills for treating ill people using her Qi energy.

During her travels, Yang Meijun also met a nun who could meditate for hours and hours and who was able to stop her menstruation cycle. This meant that she could transfer all her blood to Qi, and so her body and energy was very strong. Some of the monks that she met did not sleep at night. Instead they sat on cushions and meditated throughout the night until daybreak. This way they never lost their Jing through seminal emission.

Both a woman and a mother, Meijun understood how the body worked, but she also understood more deeply than most the workings of Qi. She had learned through her Qigong practice that there are three types of Qi. When we practise Qigong, the first energy that we gather is the sexual energy, called Jing. For women, this is connected with the blood. For men, this is connected with the sperm. If a person keeps practising and does not lose their Jing, then it will be transformed in the body to become Qi.

If the Qi is conserved, then it will rise upward in the body to become Shen. Shen means spirit. With high level Qigong masters, you can see that they have strong Qi, with shiny skin and supple bodies and movements. You can see their spirit or Shen energy in their eyes and manner. This cultivation and preservation of the sexual energy also helps promote longevity. The Daoists would use Qigong to help prolong their lives and become in balance with nature and the universe.

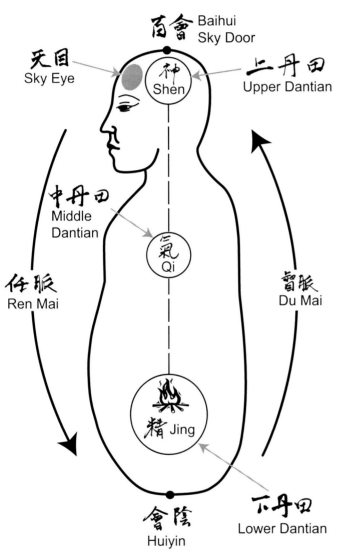

When the Shen develops, it reaches the highest level of spiritual development which is called Xu. Xu means emptiness. When a person reaches this level, their Sky Eye will become opened, they can see the colours of Qi and can even see inside a person's body, their channels and internal organs. Because the Qi has been transformed from Jing to Shen to Xu, it is quite powerful. High level masters can use Qi transmission to cure sick people, using their own energy to release blockages and help the Qi flow in the patient.

When reaching this state of develop-ment, the acupuncture point Baihui (which means Sky Door) opens and a person will find that they can receive messages from great distances or know when something is going to happen before it actually takes place. The Wild Goose Qigong skill in particular stimulates this area and helps cultivate and open the Yintang point. For this to happen, however, it takes a great deal of Qigong practice, nutrition and proper rest to create blood and sperm (Jing). People who do not practise Qigong will easily become tired when they release too much Jing. Practice of Qigong can create the vital energy needed to maintain a healthy body and even prolong life.

From her many years of Qigong practice, Yang Meijun had reached this level and it saved not only her life but others' lives as well. Once, during the war, she had to pretend to be dead in order to escape the enemy. As a result, she and another person were buried alive. To save herself, she held her breath and was able to do this for a long while because her body could breathe not only through the lungs but through the pores of her body. After she was sure that the Japanese had left, she dug herself and the other person out and saved both of their lives because of her Dayan Qigong practice.

After eight bitter years, the Japanese finally lost the war and left China. It had been a hard time, and during the war she had lost contact with her son who was seventeen at that time. She and her husband decided to return to Beijing which was much changed from when she had left. Everywhere there were sad people, many of whom had become addicted to opium through the Japanese. They even used to sell it to little children in candy as a way of making the people not resist them. However, life went on and people began to make their living and pick up the pieces of their lives.

China had lost its Imperial rulers and now had to find a new government to lead them. Although the Japanese had left, it was now the Nationalists (Guo Min Party) and the Communists who were fighting. Eventually, however, the Communists took over and it seemed a hopeful time. Yang Meijun still practised her skill secretly every night, keeping her promise to her grandfather. Throughout all the turmoil and change around her, the one thing constant in her life was her Qigong practice. By this time, her potential had developed enormously. She could see people's auras and predict things before they happened, even though she never let people know this.

Beyond the
Cultural
Revolution

After the Japanese left and the Nationalists (Guo Min Party) lost their fight against the Communists, Mao Ze Dong took over as the leader of China. There were many changes as power was shifted from landowners to the peasants. It was a confusing time for the people as most had already lost everything in the war with the Japanese. Scholars who had devoted their lives to studying the classics were now forced to dig in fields or work in factories. Farmers who did not know how to write their names were now put in positions of power and leadership. The people, following Mao Ze Dong, now had to forget the old ways of their ancestors and long revered philosophers, whether they wanted to or not. Families were separated and new loyalties created as China's ancient laws were rewritten.

In 1965 the Cultural Revolution started. Everyone was being criticised, even Yang Meijun. They criticised her for being superstitious and for worshipping Guan Yin and for her study of Daoism. She did not escape punishment and often they would make her stand for hours and hours as they shouted at her and criticised her. However, because of her skill, she was able to close her mind and treat it as if it were standing meditation. One time, one of the Red Guards picked up a stone and threw it at her, but because of her quick reflexes, she was able to dodge the stone and thus avoid injury.

These were hard times for nearly everyone. She saw many Qigong and martial art masters criticised, injured and even executed. One martial arts master who knew Hard Qigong (a style of Qigong used to develop the external body, muscles and bones) was told to stand on a table. The Red

Guards proceeded to hit his lower legs with clubs while taunting him. As they hit him they would jeer, "Let's see how strong you are. Let's see how long you can stand it." The beating was so brutal that the man never fully recovered and he was crippled for the rest of his life.

Because she had kept her promise to her grandfather, no one knew that Yang Meijun practised Qigong and so she managed to survive the ten years of the Cultural Revolution without too much damage. Slowly even the years of the Cultural Revolution passed and things were beginning to change. Grandmaster Yang was now over eighty years old and she knew that it was time that she should pass on her family's skill.

These were different times from those in which her grandfather had lived. They were also different times from those in which the Daoist Monks of the Kunlun Mountains had lived before him. Yang Meijun knew that part of understanding Dao was how to adapt yourself to survive, like the willow bending itself to the wind. She wanted her family's skill to survive and it was her duty to keep her promise to both her grandfather and to Guan Yin to make sure that it did.

Grandmaster Yang Meijun teaching in the park in Beijing, China

However, if she passed her skill on to only one other person, as those masters before her had done, then what would happen if the person she chose were killed or had an accident. She had seen so much death in her life not to consider this a real possibility. After much thought and meditation, she decided that the right way was to slowly open some of the skill to the public. She decided that the skill she would open should be some of the forms, like Dayan Qigong and Kunlun Twining Hand Bagua. The healing and energy transmission skills she had learned, she would keep for persons whom she considered had special potential. With her Sky Eye skill being highly developed from over seventy years of practise, she could see more about people than others could. It was not only illness and disease that she could diagnose, she could also tell whether someone had a sincere heart and what kind of future they had.

In 1978 she began teaching in Beijing's Sun Wu Man Park. When Grandmaster Yang, a tiny grey-haired old lady with a straight posture and energetic step, walked into the park, there would be many people gathered waiting for her. When they saw her, they would form a line before her and one by one tell her of their health problems. Without actually physically touching them, she would then put her hand to where the pain was. Quickly, they began to feel better and upon leaving they were visibly much happier than before. With some of the people, she did not even ask them about their problems, but instead told them what the problem was.

One she told, "You have been working very hard and have exhausted your kidneys. You need to maintain them, otherwise within three years you will not be able to walk." Another she told, "Your lungs have been blocked. The Qi does not flow there, that is why you feel pressure in your chest." After her treatments, they all felt much better and more comfortable. On one occasion, an old gentleman who looked very ill said, "I have been travelling from North to South, looking everywhere for a doctor who can treat my ailment. So far, no doctor has been able to rid me of it. Laozi, (a respectful term meaning 'teacher') if you can help me, I will pay whatever you want."

She answered him, "No need to worry about money. The most important thing is your health. I have retained my Qi for more than 70 years and if I do not use it now, it will be wasted. Now is the right time for my skill to be used. The last ten years of the Cultural Revolution have caused many people pain and suffering and this has affected their health. You are not alone, but now is the time to correct this."

So making the shape of two sword fingers, she pointed to different areas of his body. After a few minutes, he told her that he felt much better. He said, "My body feels much lighter and my head doesn't hurt at all." Yang smiled and replied, "You still need some more treatment. According to the principles of Chinese Medicine, when we feel pain it is because the Qi does not flow through the channels. So you will then feel pain and stiffness. Maybe you will even feel sick in your stomach. When I transmit Qi to the problem area, I stimulate the acupuncture points and this will create a reaction that will improve the condition and get rid of the negative Qi. Qi is our vital energy that maintains our lives. You cannot just use it all the time. The more you use it, the more you will become tired and exhausted. I am old and even I cannot use my Qi all of the time!"

On another day she was approached by a young man who said to her respectfully, "Old teacher, (in saying someone is old, you are paying them a compliment), I have never seen Qi being transmitted. Please can you show me and let me experience it?" Yang Meijun thought to herself that it was the right time to show the people the power of her Dayan Qigong skill. So she replied, "If you look around, you will notice that there is no wind and everything is peaceful. Now, I want you to watch that tree and see what happens." She then gestured towards a tree that was about five metres away. "I am going to use my Qi to affect it. Watch, you will see."

So saying, she raised her hand and concentrated. After a short while the tree's leaves began to move and make a rustling sound. It was as if there was a wind blowing. Everyone who had observed this was so impressed and felt privileged to have witnessed such skill. Many thought things like that happened only in old stories about magic. They all applauded her and thought to themselves how special this old lady was, still not knowing how much skill she secretly held.

She then continued, "This is my family's skill, Dayan Qigong. When you reach a high level, your Sky Eye will open, you can see people's channels and Qi flow inside their body. You will be able to see things that you normally cannot see, like colours. When your skill is even higher, your Baihui point will open and you can receive or send messages by just thinking."

For over a year, Master Yang helped many sick people and saved many lives in the park. People talked to each other, one person telling ten and the ten telling ten more. Talk of her name and amazing healing skill spread very quickly. Some people even called her Immortal Yang. Eventually, she was invited to give treatments at a hospital outside the city, and from this she earned a modest income. Because of her successful healings, the hospital became very busy. Many people waited for her treatment. The doctors were happy as the patients were recovering without medicine.

Grandmaster Yang transmitting Qi

Western medicine only treats the symptoms of a problem and misses self-healing. We are human and, like all creatures on the planet, we can help create resistance to defend against illness when we live in balance with nature. When she gave treatments, Grandmaster Yang used her Qi to clear the patient's body of toxins so that blood and Qi could flow. The patients could then recover by practising Qigong on their own. She used only her Qigong skills that had been developed over many decades to heal, not any medicines or herbs.

In the hospital, the queue was often very long. Some patients even brought sleeping rolls with them, waiting all night to see the amazing Qigong master. One day, two young men came to see Grandmaster Yang. On meeting them, she immediately spoke to the first one and said, "You have been practising lying Qigong for a long time without correct instruction. Your Qi stays in your arms and legs and sometimes at your waist, causing you pain and making you feel uncomfortable. This is what we call 'Qi in disorder'."

She then turned and continued to speak to the second boy, "Once when you practised meditation, you caught 'Cold Wind', so you feel cold inside the body, even when the weather is warm. Also, you have pressure in your chest. This makes you feel uncomfortable and sometimes you even feel sick. This we call 'Loosening the Fire and the Devil Comes In'."

Of the two young men, the first admitted that he was studying from his friend but that his friend did not have enough experience and understanding of Qigong. The other said that he had been studying from a book for over a year. Grandmaster Yang stared at them both for about ten minutes and then spoke in a chanting voice to herself. She then slapped along the channels of their bodies, from the top of their heads to their lower backs. Sometimes she pointed to their back and sometimes to their hands. She used Qi transmission over their bodies to balance their Qi.

They felt warm and could feel the negative energy flowing away. After finishing the treatment, she said to them, "Now Qigong is getting very popular. There are many styles and exercises that you can pick up, but you should stay away from any Qigong that uses the mind or visualization. This is because visualisation can easily produce side effects. Also, you should look into the history of your teacher. Many Qigong masters might not have a good enough level to teach. They will easily mislead people who want to learn."

Afterwards, Grandmaster Yang thought on this incident a lot. She wondered to herself how many others there were who were suffering side effects from practising Qigong. She thought, "It is because they do not know how to practise Qigong properly. I am already over eighty years old and it seems the right time to develop my family's skill of Dayan Qigong. It should help more people, rather than just being kept within the family." She then resigned from the hospital and began to go to the park to start her Qigong teaching. It seemed that fate had brought the two boys to her so that she could develop another path.

The days passed peacefully and she helped many people who came to her for healing and study. One day, a policeman came to her home. When he saw her he said, "Oh, you are Yang Meijun!" She replied, "As you already know, there is no point in asking." The policeman continued, "You charge people for treatments. Have you got a licence for this?" To this Master Yang did not say anything. So he asked her, "How much do you charge?", to which she replied, "I don't know." The policeman then laughed and said, "According to our records, you charge two yuan per person."

She said, "You have already investigated, so I don't need to answer you." The policeman then started to pressure her and make her tell him how she treated the people. She replied she treated people by stimulating their acupuncture points. He said, "That will kill people!". She said, "If I kill anyone, you can kill me! However, I have treated hundreds of people and so far no one has died."

The policeman was very cocky and he walked around her in a circle, looking at her as she sat. "You are so small and old, how can you fix people?" She looked back at him shrewdly. "I have helped many people with different kinds of illness. Even people with hypertension."

When she said that, the policeman stopped and then said, "My Chief Inspector at the station is in bed suffering from hypertension at this moment. I will give you this opportunity and see how well you can treat people." Grandmaster Yang nodded, gathered some things from inside her home and followed the policeman without speaking. Soon they arrived at the station.

When they arrived, the man was unconscious. Master Yang began to work on him using massage and Qi transmission. After a while, his face changed from its dark colour to a slightly redder colour. His eyes opened and began to focus. He said to Yang, "I am alright now. You can leave, go home."

She said, "Oh, but it's not that easy. I am ready for prison now." With that, she gestured to the clothing that she had brought with her. The Chief Inspector and policeman looked at each other with frowns. They did not understand what she meant. She said, "I came in innocent, but in case anyone else says anything to insult my name, I need a document to prove that I can treat people."

The Chief Inspector said, "But we cannot provide a medical certificate here. It is not our area." Yang did not say anything, but sat down on a chair and waited. In the end, the Chief gave in and said that he would write a letter for her. "I will write this letter and the police will not cause you any more problems."

At that moment, one of the policemen from outside came in to say that a group of people had come for Grandmaster Yang. News of the police escorting her from her home had spread and her students had come to help her. However, in a few moments, the policeman escorted Grandmaster Yang out to her friends and students. In her hand she held a letter which said that she was really using Qigong to help people and was not tricking them.

A Miracle

Following the incident with the police, Grandmaster Yang became more open with her Dayan Qigong teaching. She set up her first Dayan Qigong Centre. When she began her class, she immediately attracted a lot of students. Locally, people in Beijing came to know of her high level skill when she set up her Dayan Qigong Centre there. Many people also came from all over China to register and study with her as well. Of those who came, she observed them all and how they practised. Some were more talented and practised harder. These she chose to be her close students and eventually she let them go out to teach for her and help spread the Dayan Qigong skill. Many of these would live with her for a time, following her to wake up at 3am in the morning for what was called the 'hard practice'.

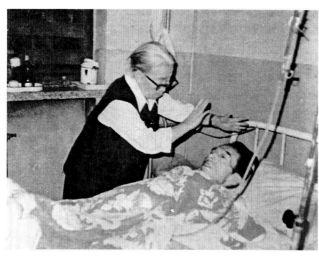

Grandmaster Yang transmitting Qi to a patient

On one occasion when practising in the park, a young person came running up to her and said, "Laozi! Laozi! My father has had an accident. Please, can you help him?" The woman continued, "I heard that you can transmit Qi to people and save their lives!" When Yang Meijun arrived at the hospital, the patient was completely wrapped in bandages, with many tubes sticking in his body. It was obvious that the situation was critical. The doctor on duty, Dr. Shen Chun Chang, told her, "His blood pressure is down to a very dangerous level. His body temperature is up very high and the brain and liver have both suffered serious damage." He continued , "His cheek bones are broken and he is suffering from urine poisoning." It was obvious to everyone there that this man's life was coming to an end, and that he was about to die.

Yang Meijun was quiet as she examined the patient. It took her nearly five minutes and then she turned to his family and said, "Take all the bandages and tubes away. I think that I can help." Of course this shocked the doctor and he refused. However, the man's family insisted and argued that with his Western medicine he had done all he could. Despite this, the patient had reached a critical level. So what could he do? He also wanted the patient to recover.

After the bandages and tubes had been taken away, Yang Meijun put her hand on the Renzhong point (the acupuncture point between the nose and the patient's mouth) and the other hand at the upper Dantian (the forehead). She stayed like this for over ten minutes, and then the patient began to cough up sputum. After twenty minutes, he began to release urine. Two hours later his blood pressure went back up, and he began to regain consciousness. All this greatly surprised everyone, especially Dr. Shen. He could not understand what had made the situation change.

Master Yang went back to the hospital to visit the patient every day and spent half an hour transmitting Qi to him, both to rid his body of the negative Qi and to recharge the positive energy. By the third day his temperature and blood pressure were near normal, and by the fourth day, he could move his arms and legs and his mind was starting to clear. Finally, by the fifth day, his condition was under control and he could also speak a few sentences. The whole situation was watched closely by Dr. Shen. He suddenly realised that after many years of studying and treating people with Western medicine, he only understood one side of health.

Chinese Qigong is very powerful and does not use any medicine. This raised Dr Shen's curiosity, and he wanted to find out more about how Qigong worked. He was impressed that this little, tiny lady, who was ninety years old, could save someone so critically near death. So Dr. Shen politely asked Yang Meijun to accept him as her student. Yang smiled and said, "You already know Western medicine. If you also study my Qigong, you will be like a tiger with wings!" She then said, "Let me choose an auspicious day, and I will accept you as one of my students." So Yang increased her fold of close students who were learning her skill. This time the student was a doctor of Western medicine.

Because of her powerful Qigong treatments and her beautiful Dayan Qigong skill, Yang Meijun attracted a lot of attention from all over China, especially from the Chinese government. After losing so much in the Cultural Revolution, they were keen to restore and preserve their culture. Now all these cultural skills, like Qigong and martial arts, were not only being protected by the government, but they were being promoted as well.

The Chinese Qigong Scientific Research Society made her an honorary member and asked her many times to give seminars and treatments. Many universities also gave her honorary professorships for research into Qigong and for teaching her family skill. One day, Yang Meijun accepted an offer from Wuhan

Eastern Lake University to teach her Dayan Qigong skill there. It was here that she founded her second Centre. Wuhan is known by everyone for its bad weather and is known as one of China's "Four Stoves" because in the summer it is so hot and in the winter it is so cold. Her students could not understand why she wanted to go there and were afraid that she would not be used to the extreme weather. However, she had her own reasons.

Due to all the publicity through newspapers, magazines and even television, she was now very famous throughout China. It was because many people spoke of her and her name had become so well known, that her son, whom she had lost contact with since the Japanese war, was able to locate and contact her. Her husband had been dead for many years and she wanted to take his ashes back to his hometown to worship and pay her respects. As soon as she arrived in Wuhan, she went immediately to meet with her son who had come to see her. She refused to see anyone or even go out. After so many years apart, she wanted to enjoy this time to be a family again and to recharge her energy after the long journey.

Chapter 2

Michael Tse

Meeting Grandmaster Yang

Yang Meijun taught in Wuhan for three years and this time was the high point in her teaching. Her name and story appeared in the newspapers and attracted many people, particularly young people who came to her from many different places. I was one of them. I had heard about Grandmaster Yang Meijun through the many Qigong magazines that had started to be published in China and Hong Kong. This was the early eighties. I had already been studying Wing Chun for many years, but I wanted to develop my internal energy. When I first read about Grandmaster Yang and her story, I was so excited, just as everyone else who reads it is. I had begun studying a Hard Style Qigong and I talked to my Sifu about wanting to learn soft Qigong. He said that I should study Dayan Qigong and it turned out that he knew Grandmaster Yang. After some weeks, he arranged an introduction for me, and I made plans to travel to Wuhan to visit her.

Michael with his teacher Grandmaster Yang Meijun

It was a very difficult place to find and it was a long journey as travelling was not as easy as it is now. First, I flew from Hong Kong to Wuhan and then asked people how I could get to Dong Hu. Eventually I found the train station and finally walked from Dong Hu train station to where she lived. She lived at the University in a house on campus. It was very quiet there, with lots of fresh air and no pollution. I already felt the Qi was very good in this area, fit for a good Master.

As I came up to the house, I saw people practising outside. When I went into her house, I walked into a very big room and introduced myself to a young man there, saying that I had travelled from Hong Kong to meet Master Yang. He went away and came back in a few minutes to take me to meet her. She invited me into her room where she was sitting on the sofa in lotus position. My heart was already beating very fast. I had heard many, many stories and read so much about her, now here I was meeting her face to face. Everybody who has meets her has this feeling. I walked in and straight away knelt down in front of her and gave her the gifts I had brought with me. Kneeling down made me smaller than her, as she is quite a small lady. This also showed my respect.

Although my Mandarin was not very fluent at that time, it was even worse than usual as I was so nervous. We started a conversation. She asked me my name and I told her. You could already tell that she was familiar with people visiting her from many different areas. I rarely looked at her directly, just glanced at her, but I noticed that she did not look her age. At the most she only looked fifty plus and her face was very clear and smooth. You could see the power in her face and her eyes had very strong spirit. We started to talk about my family, how many brothers and sisters I had and then we finally came to the subject of my studies.

Without me having told her anything about my own training, she said, "You have too much martial art energy and have not developed your spiritual and healing side. All your energy is going to your bone, muscle and skin. Not enough to your mind." I did not know how to answer. I had not told her anything about my martial art studies, so I was very impressed that she could see this. After she had been talking for a while, I could smell a very strong fragrance, one that smelt like jasmine. I thought that there must be some flowers nearby. I also felt peaceful since I had walked in. I later came to know that this was a high level Qigong called, "Opening the Chest Fragrance Transmission". When the body is healthy, then the body will release a fragrant Qi, like a flower, but if you are unhealthy, then the body will release negative Qi which can smell like rotten fruit or sick. So now I know when I meet people whether they are ill or healthy straight away, because I can smell their Qi. From the different smells, Yang Sifu taught me that you can diagnose different illnesses.

As we continued to talk, she offered me some advice saying, "You need to be more relaxed to develop your spiritual side otherwise it will be no good for your future and you will be unbalanced."

I then said to her, "Yang Laozi, I would like to study with you."

She smiled and said, "You will be very good in the future. You have potential. But there is one thing you are always missing." She did not tell me what it was and I did not ask. Looking back, I now know what it was though. From that day, I stayed with her at her home and began to learn the way to live in mainland China. Life was very simple. We practised in the morning and evening, not much in the afternoon. I started with the Dayan Qigong 1st 64. The most interesting thing was training in the middle of the night – at three o'clock in the morning. This was to open our Sky Eye potential. This was an area which I had never developed.

I remember once when she was sitting in the middle of the room with all the students around her and after a few minutes, she asked us what we had seen. Some people said they had seen yellow or red colours, and some said they had seen smoke, but I could see nothing. So I knew my Sky Eye had not been opened. After I had been practising for awhile, though, I started to see the colour around her. Once my Sky Eye had opened, I started to see things differently.

Once when I was talking to her about the Sky Eye, she said to me, "Some people's Sky Eye is easy to open and some people will take a long time. Some people's Sky Eye will never open." She continued to say, "The first time I saw you, I knew you had potential. That is why I let you stay to study with me."

I stayed with her nearly a month and finished a lot of basic forms and then had to go back to Hong Kong, where I was still working in the Royal Hong Kong Police Force. From that moment, whenever Grandmaster Yang had any courses or seminars, I did my best to join in. Even when I moved to the United Kingdom, I still went to visit her nearly every year. She is like my grandmother. Every time I visited her, we talked a lot apart from training. She has taught me how to behave and to have a good heart. She has also taught me how to study more Buddhist and Daoist philosophy. This has helped me know how to handle difficult situations and understand people. So when something unexpected happens or things do not go how I plan, I try to remember the lessons she has taught me.

Michael Tse with Grandmaster Yang and other students in China

When we can accept that things are always changing and understand how each action has a consequence, then we know how to take it easy. She also taught me how to heal other people, how to educate others and do more good things. I try to give my students the same education and not only teach the

Qigong movements I have learned. I also try to show them the philosophy and principles behind it as well. When they can understand the five elements and Yin and Yang theory and apply this to their Qigong and their life, then their skill will be deeper than just movement. Qigong is about balance. To have good health we also have to balance our emotions and lifestyle and have consideration for others.

I have always said when training my instructors that having a good heart is more important than having good skill. Good skill can be learned but having a good heart is much harder to acquire. But with more practice, it will happen.

History &
Chinese Philosophy of
Wild Goose Qigong

History & Chinese Philosophy of Wild Goose Qigong

Wild Goose Qigong is a profound skill that connects with Buddhism, Daoism, Chinese philosophy of the Five Elements, Yin/Yang theory and Chinese Medical theory. It was created by the Buddhist monk named Dao An, who lived in the Kunlun Mountain Range in China during the Jin dynasty, over 1,800 years ago. On this famous mountain range, which was a spiritual retreat for many Daoists, there also lived many wild geese. While observing these beautiful birds they began to imitate their movements.

Today, the most popular and famous form in this system is Wild Goose (Dayan) Qigong. "Da" means big and "Yan" means wild goose. So the system is named Kunlun Dayan referring to the mountain range where it was created and to the wild geese who inspired the many movements in the forms. There are actually two sets of Wild Goose Qigong movements each containing 64 movements.

Do you know why we have sixty-four movements and not forty-five or even one hundred? Numbers are very special for Chinese people. Each number has its own meaning and energy, particularly the number eight. Eight relates to the eight trigrams that were discovered by Fu Hsi who lived during 2953-2838 BC. The story goes that one day while walking along a river, Fu Hsi saw a horse emerge from the river with markings on its back which are now known as the Earlier Heaven Bagua (called Ho To).

There is also a Later Heaven Bagua (called Lo Shu) which was discovered by his predecessor, Da Yu. After Da Yu had managed to bring floodwaters under control by building dykes and canals, he saw a tortoise emerge from the waters of the River Lo and on its back were patterns which translated into those of the Later Heaven Bagua.

All this sounds very complicated and a bit mystical, but really it is quite simple. Just as a tree will have the history of the seasons recorded in its rings, animals also adapt to weather and seasonal conditions. If it is a particularly cold winter, animals like deer and bears will grow a thicker coat. Other animals also adapt to changes in nature in similar ways.

The Later Heaven Bagua is used to show the nature of changing things, like the orbit of the earth, the constellations and weather. Using this, we can predict things that will happen. This is the outside of things and the future. The Earlier Heaven Bagua relates to the inside of things, like human nature and understanding why people and animals behave in the way they do. This can help us behave better in society.

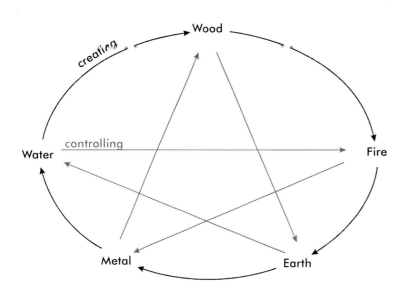

These original eight trigrams are the foundation of the Book of Changes, called the Yijing (also known as the I Ching). When we multiply eight by eight, we get sixty four, the same as the sixty-four trigrams in the Yijing. So Wild Goose Qigong also relates to the Yijing and Bagua. Today, many people use the Yijing to make predictions. By observing and following nature, we can adapt ourselves to the seasons, eating and sleeping at the right times, keeping our emotions balanced so that we have harmony in the body.

I also mentioned the Five Elements and Yin/Yang theory. Within both the Lo Shu and Ho Tu, the number five is the centre. The Chinese have Five Elements:- wood, water, metal, fire and earth. Each of these elements relates to an organ in our body. They also relate to a direction on the compass and to the five seasons. There are many more connections as well, such as the five colours, five tastes, five emotions, etc. In the following chart you can see how the five tastes, five emotions and five seasons are all connected with the directions and to our five major internal organs.

For higher level Qigong practice and study, we can use the Five Elements to help us diagnose illness, find the best direction to practise for certain illnesses, etc. However, in the beginning, we do not have to worry about this.

The Characteristics of the Five Elements

WOOD	FIRE	EARTH	METAL	WATER
Liver	Heart	Spleen	Lung	Kidney
Gall Bladder	Small Intestine	Stomach	Large Intestine	Urinary Bladder
Green	Red/Orange	Yellow/Brown	White/Gold	Blue/Black
Shouting	Laughing	Singing/Talking	Weeping	Groaning/Sighing
Anger	Over-excitement	Worry, Security	Sorrow, Sad	Fear
(Love, Warm)	(Stable)	(Decision)	(Happiness)	(Power and Will)
Sour	Bitter	Sweet	Spicy	Salty
Rancid	Scorched	Fragrant	Rotten	Putrid
Spring	Summer	Long Summer	Autumn	Winter
Tendon	Pulse	Muscle	Skin and Hair	Bone
Eye	Tongue	Mouth	Nose	Ear
Life	Gas	Compound	Solid	Liquid
East	South	Centre	West	North
Birth	Growth	Conservation	Gathering	Storage
Three	Two	Five	Four	One

When we practise, we will stimulate each of these five organs so that they become healthy just by correctly following the movements. In addition, the movements will direct the Qi, so we do not need to try to move the Qi with our mind. If you remember, my Sifu said earlier that doing any visualisation in Qigong can easily lead to side effects.

Taiji symbol showing Yin and Yang moving together

Most of you will be familiar with the terms Yin and Yang. Yin means dark, soft and is correlated with female. Yang means light, hard and is correlated with male. In Qigong, we have both a Yin and a Yang side. The Yang side is the movements, which are active and which rid the body of toxins and gather fresh Qi. The Yin side is the meditation, which is passive and which collects and stores the Qi.

The symbol for Yin and Yang has a dot inside each section, symbolising that there is Yin inside Yang and Yang inside Yin. Everything in nature has both a Yin and a Yang side. Without this balance, it would either break or not have enough substance to exist. When we come to the fullest point, then the energy changes to become the opposite. If we can understand the duality of Yin and Yang, then we can apply this to our Qigong practice as well when we know more.

How To Practise

How To Practise

The proper name of this form is Dayan Qigong, however, it is so commonly known now as Wild Goose Qigong, that I often refer to it by this name as well. Both terms are correct, but sometimes the English version is more convenient for those who do not speak Chinese. I use both throughout the book.

Traditionally, Chinese internal arts and martial art skill were passed down by word of mouth from teacher to student. When things were written down, it would have been kept secret and been kept as a closely guarded treasure. So if things were not written down, how could students remember all the names of the movements for the different forms? It was usual to make the names or knowledge into a poem that had a special rhythm which made it easy to remember and repeat.

In the Dayan Qigong form, the movements are like the story of a wild goose. The movements imitate those of a wild goose waking up, stretching, flying across the sea, looking for food, looking for the nest and then sleeping peacefully and recovering Qi. This is the way I learned the forms with Grandmaster Yang as they all have a poem to remember them by. I often use this same method to memorise things for my Feng Shui and Bazi studies.

Skim Over
the Sea

Today, we are more lucky and it is very convenient to study now. But somehow, I still prefer the traditional ways. No video or book can replace the special relationship between the teacher and student or pass on the higher level principles of the skill. However, books are invaluable reference tools. I have over two thousand books and still find it hard to resist going into a bookstore whenever

I am in China. That is why I have written this book for you. I hope it can help improve your studies and understanding of the Dayan Qigong. When you understand something, you will appreciate it more.

There are two sets of Dayan Qigong Movements, the 1st 64 and also the 2nd 64. For the purposes of this book, we will only cover the 1st 64 movements. These first movements relate to the post-natal Qi in our body. Post-natal Qi is the energy that comes after you are born. Since you were born, you may have been ill or injured. These problems come from your diet, environment or through your lifestyle habits, like stressful work, lack of exercise, injury, etc. By practising the 1st 64 movements, we can help heal these problems by helping to release the ill energy from the body.

The 2nd 64 movements deal with pre-natal illness or problems that we inherit. For instance, if heart problems run in your family, then there is more chance of this affecting you than someone who does not have a history of this problem. Just like a tree, if it is not healthy, then the fruit it bears will also not be healthy.

We always learn the 1st and 2nd 64 sets in order. The movements contained in the 1st 64 set are larger and more open than the more subtle movements in the 2nd 64 series. These larger movements help us to clear the channels in the body so that the Qi and blood can flow smoothly. In Dayan Qigong there are many different types of movements that are used to help us release the negative energy from the body. These include dropping down on the heels, fluttering, pushing and flicking the hands. Some of the movements are vigorous while others are more gentle. When we drop our weight down on the heels, all the Qi is concentrated and will release through the channels and the Yongquan point in the sole of the foot. Fluttering movements help stimulate all the internal organs and the channels in the arms. Smoothing Qi assists the Qi in flowing along the Yin and Yang channels of the body.

After we release the negative energy, we then gather fresh energy. We do this by bringing Qi to the acupuncture points which act like doors and windows to let it into the body. You will see that Dayan Qigong uses many acupuncture points, particularly for the kidneys and lungs. Kidneys store the essence in our body and our lungs regulate Qi. We gather fresh Qi throughout the form so that the three Dantians (Lower, Middle and Upper) are continually being refreshed. As the toxins and old Qi are released, new Qi replaces them and internal washing of the organs and channels continues.

The 1st 64 movements gently stretch the body and create more flexibility in the waist and hips through squatting, bending and turning movements. By moving up and down we can also help the body and brain to balance the energy so that we do not have problems later with blood pressure and dizziness. When we are more supple, the Qi can flow better in the body, opening channels and acupuncture points and helping to restore balance. The waist and hips are the first parts of our bodies to become stiff. Often you will see older people who walk with a stick or cannot walk at all. This is because the Qi no longer flows in this area.

Many people today take vitamin supplements or even hormones, hoping that this will stop their bones from becoming weak. I personally do not recommend people to rely too much on these things. If we do not move and only try to rely on supplements to make us healthy, eventually we will become ill. To be healthy, we need to move. Have you ever had a car and not driven it for a long time? Once, when I was in China, I came back and my car battery was dead even though I had not left the lights on or otherwise used it. It turns out that my car alarm had slowly used the battery power while it was standing idle. Because the car had not been driven, the battery had not had a chance to recharge itself. So it is the same for the human body. When we do not move, we feel heavy because our circulation is sluggish. The less we move, the more tired we feel.

Everything in life is about balance. We need to balance our lives, sometimes moving and exercising and sometimes resting. But if we do not move we will have problems, and our joints will become stiff, like a rusty door hinge. Qigong is the oil for our bodies, lubricating the joints when they get rusty. The gentle movements of Qigong are good for all ages and levels of fitness.

Questions About Practice

How many movements should I learn at one time?

Wild Goose Qigong is a profound skill and contains many different kinds of movements. In the beginning it may be a bit confusing or frightening to learn so many different movements. But the best way is to take things one step at a time and go at a pace with which you are comfortable. However, it is still best not to learn too many movements at one time. Some will find that one movement is enough to practise for a few days or even a week. You should slowly build up the movements one by one so that your body can digest and coordinate them with relaxation. In the beginning you may be a bit stiff and find some of the squatting or balancing postures awkward, but if you keep practising, you will become more familiar with the movements. Eventually, the movements should be like your good friend and be comfortable to you.

Sometimes people are so hungry to learn something new that they never taste what they have eaten, let alone digest it before going on to their next meal. I sometimes have a student in class who will ask, "Can I learn more?" Actually, they miss the point. Perhaps they could learn more movements, but are they able to understand the principle behind the movement and to do the movement with relaxation and coordination. It takes time for the movements to sink into your body and for the right Qi to develop. If your channels are not all open, then the Qi will not flow as smoothly as it could. This takes time and practice.

So do not be in a hurry for quick results. The goal of Qigong should be good health, and you can only do this step by step and by regular practice.

How do I direct the Qi?

When you practise Wild Goose Qigong, you do so naturally. You do not need to think about directing the Qi as the movements will direct it to where it should go. For instance, when we open the arms in the first movement, 'Spread Wings', we do not have to think about opening the lungs and Qihu points. In the movement, 'Wind Hand Around Head and Ears', the Laogong point in the palm smooths the Qi along the Yang channels in the arm and around the acupuncture points at the back of the head. If we had to constantly think about opening a particular channel or acupuncture point or think about directing Qi to the Sky Eye, we would be too concentrated to relax and let the mind go. This is why it is not necessary to use any visualisation in Wild Goose Qigong. So when you practise, try and relax both the mind and body and let any distracting thoughts go. This is the natural way.

I have studied Taijiquan for many years. Do I practise Wild Goose Qigong in the same way that I practise Taijiquan?

Taijiquan is a martial art. There are many different styles of Taijiquan, like Sun, Wu, Yang and Chen style. They all have their own way of handling energy. Qigong is a health exercise and so the attitude and purpose is different. That is not to say Taijiquan is not good for health, but this was not why it was created. So Qigong should not be practised with a Taijiquan attitude. Dayan Qigong is concerned with opening and dredging the channels of stagnant (ill) Qi and gathering fresh Qi. The movements in Dayan Qigong connect with many acupuncture points and help smooth the channels.

Michael Tse leading students in the movement "Wind Hand Around Head and Ears"

The most important thing is that we should practise in a relaxed manner so that the movements, breath and Qi are all connected. If we go too slow, it is like a puppy always straining at a leash, wanting to move forward but held back. If we go too fast, then the Qi cannot keep up with the movement and it becomes like aerobic exercises.

What should I wear to do my practice?

You do not need to wear any special clothing to practise Qigong. Try to wear something that is comfortable, though. Loose clothing will let your body breathe more and flat shoes will help you to keep your balance when standing on the balls of the feet or balancing the weight on one leg.

Where should I practise?

I always encourage people to practise outside if the weather is nice. In this way you will gather more energy from nature. If you find it is too cold or the weather is bad, then you can practise inside with the window slightly open. This will help change the air as you release negative energy. When we practise, we take fresh Qi from the air around us, therefore, you should practise in a good environment. Some people are lucky and can practise in their back gardens. Others may live near a busy road where there is pollution or too much noise. For myself, I usually go to a park to practise as there are less distractions and more space. There, I can take the energy from all the plants and trees around me. Qigong should connect with nature and help make us more balanced.

How long should I practise?

How long you practise is up to you. However, you should listen to your body. Sometimes when we practise, even if we are tired, it will help us feel more energetic. Many times I have experienced this. I travel a lot to teach and can sometimes get over-tired. I find, though, when I go out to practise, if I just begin to do the first few movements of Dayan Qigong, then I will start to feel better. By the time I am half way through, I am more awake and feel my mind more clear.

However, if we come to the point where we are using energy to practise and feel more tired than when we began, then we should stop and leave it for another time. In this situation, it is better to do some meditation and then go to sleep. Then, the next day when you are rested, you can practise. So why does this happen? It is because you over-used your energy. Instead of having some left to draw upon to do the exercises, you have exhausted yourself. You have come to the point where you are using more energy to practise, than what you can gather.

This is one of the differences between Qigong and other forms of exercise, like weight training and aerobics. These use tension to create muscle and burn fat. Qigong uses relaxation combined with movement and breathing to cultivate the Qi. If we practise a movement too fast, then the Qi cannot keep up with the movement. If we practise too slow, then the movement becomes stagnant. So we want our movement to be balanced. When practising Wild Goose Qigong the movement should be natural, not overly slow like a Taijiquan movement, and not too fast, like a fitness exercise.

Should I practise if I am ill?

Often I am asked if we should practise when we are ill. Qigong practice will help us release the negative energy and gather positive energy. So, yes, if you want to recover more quickly, then move. When I have a cold or fever, I will do as much of the form as I am able to without exhausting myself. Many of the movements, like 'Spread Wings' and 'Grasp Qi', are very good for opening the chest and helping the breathing. Even in cases of back problems or other injuries and illness, the way to recover is to move. Maybe you need to do more simple Qigong movements, like Balancing Gong, and then work up to the Wild Goose, but eventually all the movement you are doing will help stimulate your circulation and Qi.

Sometimes people are very ill and do not feel well enough to do the movements. Even lifting their arms above their head can be very tiring. Slowly, you can build up your strength little by little. If you do not move to release the negative Qi, it will just stay inside your body. Often Western medicine will make the body weaker. This is why it is even more important to do your Qigong practice.

I have a student who, before he began his Qigong studies, had back surgery and complete bed rest because he was in such severe pain. After the first operation they wanted to do more, and that is when he came to me to ask my advice about what he should do. I told him that if he wanted to walk in five years, then he should move. So that is what he did. He began doing Wild Goose Qigong and gradually increased his practice to include other forms. Now he can do any of the Qigong forms plus studying martial arts. (You will find his and other stories by people who have been practising Wild Goose Qigong in a later chapter. In their words, they share how studying Wild Goose Qigong has benefited them.)

Is learning the acupuncture points necessary?

The acupuncture points are like gates where energy can enter the body from outside. If these points are blocked, then the Qi cannot enter, nor can it flow along the channels where the acupuncture points are located.

In the Wild Goose Qigong movements, we will often bring the energy to a particular acupuncture point (or energy gate) to help stimulate a particular organ or function in the body. These points are also our 'markers', which will show us where our hands should be when doing the movements. For instance, in the movement 'Cloud Hands', if we do not know where the Yongquan point is, we will not understand the purpose of opening the sole of the foot when stepping forward. It is small details like these that make Wild Goose Qigong so profound, but also such an effective Qigong style for healing illness and restoring vital energy in the body.

You can refer to the table of acupuncture points before you begin to familiarise yourself with the names and locations of the points. Over time, they should become as familiar to you as your name. All it takes is practice!

How many times should I practise?

How many times you go through the movements is up to you. You should listen to your body and feel what is right for you. There will be some who have done some exercise before and so will be able to manage going through the whole form once, even more. Others may feel tired after even a few movements. We should slowly build up our Qi and go at a pace which is comfortable. Everyone is different and only you know what is best for you.

How should I breathe during practice?

In Wild Goose Qigong, we do not have to think about breathing. However, no matter which movement we are doing, we should always breathe through the nose.

I always say that the mouth is for eating and the nose is for breathing. When we close the mouth and rest the tongue at the upper palate, then we also help close the channel for the Xiao Zhou Tian to form. The breathing will also be much deeper when we breathe through the nose. We do not need to think about abdominal or deep breathing as the movements will naturally lead the Qi down to the Dantian when we are relaxed and the mouth closed. There may be other styles of Qigong or exercise in which this is different. However, for practising Wild Goose Qigong, we practise with the mouth closed.

Will I experience anything special when I practise Dayan Qigong?

Everybody is different, but it is not unusual to feel warmth and even tingling. We will feel warmth as the blood circulation improves, particularly in the hands, feet and even joints. When we feel tingling, this is because the Qi is working in that area. For instance, if you have a shoulder problem, then the Qi will go there to work to release the stale Qi that is creating the blockage. Usually, it is during meditation that we will feel this kind of sensation. This is why we should always do Shou Gong at the end of meditation, to bring the Qi back to the Dantian.

Some people may feel that their bodies are lighter with more practice. Some may feel more flexible and balanced. Others may even feel tingling or warmth in the limbs. However, we should not pay so much attention to these sensations as they are only the by-product and not the goal of Qigong practice. It is enough to know that these feelings are natural.

What happens if I feel pain when I do one of the movements?

If you feel pain when you are practising, try to listen to your body. Is it one particular movement or the whole form that is creating the pain. Sometimes when we begin to practise Dayan Qigong, we will not be as flexible as we would like. If you find you cannot bend all the way over, like in 'Twist the Toes', then bend as far as you are comfortable. If the pain is something that persists, then you should stop practice and try to find out more information as to why.

Do I always have to do the meditation when I practise. Can I do meditation on its own?

Meditation is the Yin side of our Qigong practice. We have done the movements, which are active and so we need stillness to balance the Yang. If you think about how many things we hear, see, smell, taste or feel each day, then you can see how our senses and thinking can become overloaded. The mind plays an immense role in our health. Over-thinking can cause the spleen to be damaged and cause stomach problems, disrupting the way in which nutrients are processed and distributed in the body.

The older we become, the more our energy rises to our minds, causing stress and illness. When the energy is not at the Dantian, we will feel distracted and can easily be upset by things. However, when the energy is at the Dantian, we are more grounded and calm. It is easy to see things more clearly and not make mistakes. That is why too much television and computer games for children and even adults, without the right balance of moving and rest, will affect their thinking and development.

So meditation is very important. After we do Qigong practice, we should always do meditation, otherwise we will lose the energy we have worked for because we have not settled it at our Dantian. The Dantian is our storehouse for energy. This does not mean you cannot do meditation outside of practice. I often do meditation before sleeping as it helps to calm my mind and release any stress and tensions from the day.

How is Qigong meditation different from other styles of meditation?

There are many methods of meditation within the Kunlun Dayan Qigong system. Some involve standing, some sitting, some lying down and some using the lotus position. In the beginning, we should concentrate on one or two. Sometimes you may feel tired and so you can try a sitting posture to help you relax more. Standing postures will help you develop your leg strength and make the kidneys and back stronger.

In Qigong meditation, we use different hand positions which help us to gather and direct the energy in the body. Most often the hands will be held at the Lower Dantian to help us collect more Qi here. There are also other hand positions in more advanced level meditations, and these are used for guiding Qi to other areas of the body. In some cases, the eyes will be open, but usually the eyes will be closed.

If I have already learned other styles of Qigong, can I practise Wild Goose Qigong?

You may have already tried another style of Qigong and this is fine. But you should always take care to separate them when you practise. Do not try to mix up the principles of one with the other. This could cause potential health problems as each style will have its own guidelines to follow. Never teach Qigong to anyone unless you are qualified to do so.

If I follow the book to study, will I have any health problems?

As I mentioned before, it is best to have a qualified teacher to instruct you in the movements. However, if you try to follow the movements here in the book and practise in a relaxed way, then you should be fine. Do not try to do too much and just take it easy. It is unavoidable that you may develop some bad habits from learning from a book or video, because it is not always possible to cover everything, particularly how the movements should connect and flow together. When learning like this, you are missing the observation from the teacher who can look at your movement and correct your mistakes. In the future, we will try to offer some correspondence courses on some of the Kunlun Dayan system Qigong forms I teach. These will give you more detailed instructions for a practice schedule.

Is it alright to practise if I am pregnant?

In the Dayan Qigong form, there are many bending and low squatting movements which can put too much pressure on the baby. However, if you practise gently, and do not bend over at the waist so much, then you should be alright. However, it is best to take advice and also see how you feel. If you feel at all uncomfortable or dizzy, then you should leave it for a while.

Is there anything special I should do after finishing practice?

When we have finished practising, we do Shou Gong. Shou means collecting or harvesting, and Gong means work. Standing with feet shoulder width apart and knees straight, we bring the arms to the sides of the body. Then slowly raise the arms, palms facing upwards, and collect the energy, bringing it up to the face, past the Sky Eye, and then down to the middle chest, stomach and to the Lower Dantian. We do this three times.

Shou Gong

I have said many times in my classes that Shou Gong is like a light switch for the body. When we do the relaxation before we begin our Qigong practice, the movements are exactly the same as Shou Gong. However, we do not call it this because Shou Gong refers to an ending movement or action. So if we walk into a dark room, we need to turn on the light (relaxation movement) and when we finish, we need to turn off the light (Shou Gong).

(NOTE: If you are practising one movement over and over or just repeating a particular section, then you do Shou Gong only once. This will settle the Qi enough and prepare you to begin again.)

Dayan Qigong The First 64 Movements

1. *Starting Position*

a. Stand with feet shoulder width apart, body relaxed, knees straight, eyes looking straight ahead. The focus should be relaxed.

b. Slowly raise the arms to the side of the body, palms facing upwards as if you are gathering something in the hands.

c. Bring the arms to shoulder height and above the head and lower downwards.

d. Pass palms downwards, Laogong points facing the body, past the Sky Eye, middle chest, stomach and to the Lower Dantian. Repeat three times.

e. Bring palms back behind the body, so that the Laogong points face the Huantiao points. The arms should be relaxed and the chest open. This posture helps the lungs to gather more Qi by opening the Qihu points.

When we face the Laogong point to the Huantiao point, we stimulate the Gall Bladder Channel. By opening the chest, we also open the Qihu points so that the Qi moves from here, down to the Huantiao points and on down to the Yongquan points, in the sole of the feet. This means that the Qi goes through the whole body. When the body is relaxed, it can gather more Qi from nature.

2. Spread Wings

辰翅

a   b   b (sideview)

a. Gently lean forward so that your balance comes onto the balls of your feet. Body should be forward approximately 45 degrees, not more.

b. Simultaneously: swing arms forward and up, and open to the sides of the body while still remaining balanced on the balls of your feet. The Laogong points of the hands should face each other when bending the body forward.

This movement opens the chest and lungs. Balancing on the toes means that the whole body is forced to relax and become more sensitive as it balances. If you are tense, you cannot balance. Balance in the body is good for the brain and making you younger. Bending the waist also helps to loosen and exercise the lower back.

Qihu 氣户

These points are located just below the collarbone on each side of the body and are located on the Stomach Channels. In Qigong, we will feel the sensation in the area that is a bit lower than this, in the area that is most tender when we press it.

Huantiao 環跳

Located in the indentation on either side of the buttocks on the Gall Bladder Channel.

Qihai 氣海

This point is located one and a half thumbs width below the navel. This acupuncture point relates to the Lower Dantian, a place where Qi is stored.

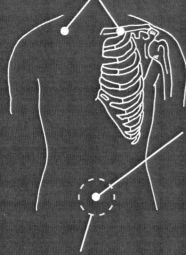

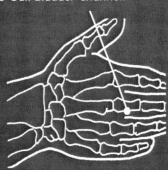

Lower Dantian 下丹田

The Lower Dantian relates to the Qihai point and is where Qi is stored.

Yintang 印堂

The Yintang point is located on the forehead between the two eyebrows and is an extra-ordinary point, not related to any channel. In Dayan Qigong, we often refer to an area called the Sky Eye which is located at the Upper Dantian. The more we practise Qigong, then we will often feel sensations and heat in the area that is above the eyebrows. This is the area of the Sky Eye and it is just above the Yintang Point.

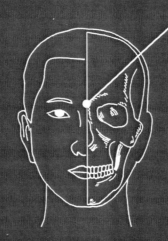

Laogong 勞宮

You can find this point by touching the middle finger to your palm. Where it touches is the area of the Laogong point. However, in Qigong, often the acupuncture point is not exactly where the Qi will be gathered or released. In this case, it is the centre of the palm where you will feel energy or heat, not only just at the Laogong point. This point is on the Pericardium Channel.

3. Close Wings

a

b

a. Following the same path as in movement 2, 'Spread Wings', close the arms, bringing the hands back to the Lower Dantian.

b. At the same time, gently bring the heels down to the floor and straighten your back.

This movement is for bringing Qi back to the Lower Dantian to develop the Dantian energy.

4. Draw Wings to the Back

Hegu 合谷

The Hegu point is found by spreading the fingers and pressing in the webbed area between the thumb and index finger. The Hegu point is on the Large Intestine Channel.

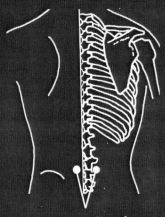

Shenshu 腎俞

These points are found on the lower back, one and a half thumbs width on either side of the second lumbar vertebrae. These points connect with the kidneys and are on the Urinary Bladder Channel.

The Five Finger Plum Blossom Claw

a

b

a. Lift the palms up (facing body) to the Middle Dantian. Keep wrists and hands completely relaxed.

b. From the Middle Dantian, push hands forward until the arms are almost but not fully extended. The Hegu points should face the Qihu points.

4. Draw Wings to the Back (cont'd)

c

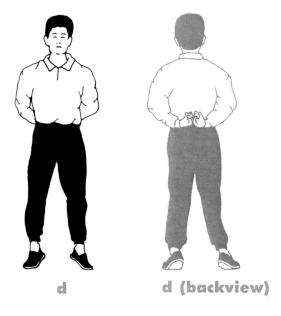

d   d (backview)

c. Open arms to the sides of the body, to shoulder height. <u>Simultaneously</u>: when arms come to the side of the body, close five fingers so that the fingertips touch together and stand on your toes. This hand position is called a Five Finger Plum Blossom Claw and is a powerful method of transmitting Qi to a particular point in the body.

d. Without hesitating, pull the hands to the back and touch the Hegu points to the Shenshu points.

We close the tips of the five fingers together in order to stimulate each of the five major internal organs as each organ connects with a particular finger. Once we have gathered fresh Qi, we bring it back to the Shenshu points to stimulate the kidneys, touching here with the Hegu points. Touching the Hegu and Shenshu points together also stimulates Qi along the Urinary Bladder and Large Intestine Channel.

5. Flick Wings

a

b

b (sideview)

a. Relax the wrists and draw the back of the hands forwards around the waist. When you reach the sides of the waist, pause for a second.

b. <u>Simultaneously</u>: flick the arms forward, releasing negative Qi, and drop down on the heels with knees bent. The elbows should be slightly in towards the waist and the wrists should be lower than the elbows so that Qi can flow downwards.

This movement gathers energy along the Belt Channel and then quickly releases it. Knees should be slightly bent to let the Qi release through the Yongquan points in the soles of the feet.

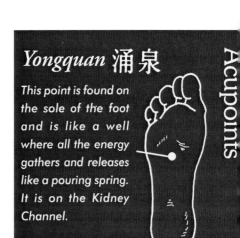

Yongquan 涌泉

This point is found on the sole of the foot and is like a well where all the energy gathers and releases like a pouring spring. It is on the Kidney Channel.

Acupoints

6. Draw Wings to the Back

a

b

a. Lift the palms up (facing body) to the Middle Dantian. Keep wrists and hands completely relaxed.

b. From the Middle Dantian, push hands out forwards till the arms are almost but not fully extended. The Hegu points should face the Qihu points.

c
d
d (backview)

c. Open arms to the sides of the body, shoulder height.

d. <u>Simultaneously</u>: when the arms come to the side of the body, close five fingers so that the fingertips touch together and stand on your toes. This hand position is called a Five Finger Plum Blossom Claw and is a powerful method of transmitting Qi to a particular point in the body. Without hesitating, pull the hands to the back and touch the Hegu points to the Shenshu points.

Same as movement 4.

7. Flick Wings

抖
膀

a   b   b (sideview)

a. Relax the wrists and draw the back of the hands forwards around the waist. When you reach the sides of the waist, pause for a second.

b. <u>Simultaneously</u>: flick the arms forward, releasing negative Qi, and drop down on the heels with knees bent. The elbows should be slightly in towards the waist and the wrists should be lower than the elbows so that Qi can flow downwards.

Same as movement 5.

8. Lift Up

上舉

a. Straighten the knees and lift the palms upwards so Laogong points are facing towards the Sky Eye.

We lift up the Qi in the palms and bring it to the Sky Eye to help open this point so that we can develop the Shen and Xu energy.

To find the Baihui point, place the lower edge of the palms at the top of the ears and lay the palms against the top of the head. Where the middle fingers meet, this is the Baihui point.

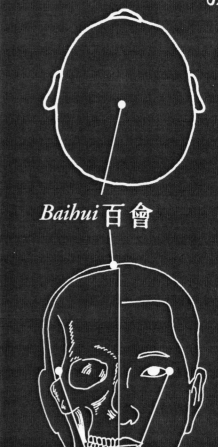

Baihui 百會

Taiyang 太陽

Taiyang means pupil crevice and is one of the strong acupuncture points. It is located one inch to the side of our eyes and is one of the extra-ordinary points not belonging to any of the regular channels.

9. Twine Fingers

合掌

a

b

a. Open the elbows outwards to the side of the head, so Laogong points face Taiyang points.

b. Continue to bring the hands above the head and twine the fingers of the palms together over the Baihui point on the top of the head. The palms should be facing down.

This movement connects both sides of the body so Qi can flow evenly.

10. Turn Palms Up

翻
掌

a

a. Keeping fingers twined, turn the palms so that they face
upwards, elbows still bent. Gently straighten elbows and
push upwards until arms are almost completely extended.
The spine should be stretched.

In this movement, we stretch the spine and the mid-section of the body so more Qi
can flow in these areas. It also helps us connect with the Heaven Qi.

11. Bend Waist

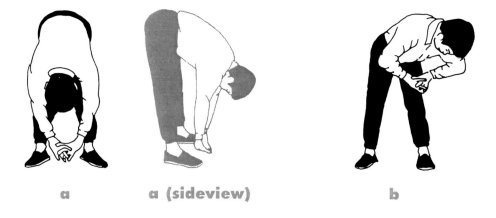

a   a (sideview)   b

a. Keeping the legs straight, bend over from the waist until the palms face the ground. If you find it difficult to push down this far, you can press down to the point where you are comfortable.

b. Moving from the waist, lift the upper body to about waist level. The palms should still be twined and near the level of your knees.

c

d

c. Push down with the waist on the left side of the body so that hands are above the left foot.

d. Lift the upper body as before to about waist level but keep on the right side of the body.

11. Bend Waist (cont'd)

e

f

e. Push hands down from the waist on the right side of the body so the hands are above the right foot.

f. Swing the body back to the front without lifting up.

We work with the kidneys and back in this movement. By keeping the knees straight, we bring all the Qi to the kidney area. When we move up and down, we do not lift the body all the way up. We only bring the hands as high as the knee and use the waist to push down. This concentrates the Qi to stimulate the channels on either side of the legs. Pushing down on the right side stimulates the right kidney and pushing down on the left side stimulates the left kidney. This movement also helps create flexibility in the legs and hips.

12. Twine Hands

纏手

a

a. <u>Simultaneously</u>: separate the palms, moving the left hand forwards and the right hand backwards and at the same time open the left foot (toes up), turning the body 90 degrees. When you open the hands, the Hegu points should face each other. When you turn, make sure you do so on the heel. The left heel acts as a pivot so that you can accurately gauge the direction as well as keeping your body grounded. The body should still be bent at the waist, but should now be facing forward 90 degrees from the original position.

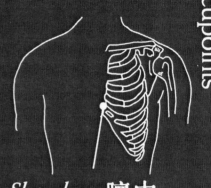

Shanzhong 膻中

The Shanzhong point is located at the Middle Dantian directly between the two nipples, in the deeper area on the breastbone. It is on the Ren Channel.

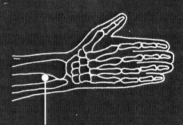

Waiguan 外關

This point is located on the upper side of the forearm, two thumb widths below the crease in the wrist. It is on the Triple Warmer Channel.

Neiguan 内關

This point is located on the inside forearm two thumb widths below the crease at the bottom of the wrist and is on the Pericardium Channel.

12. Twine Hands (cont'd)

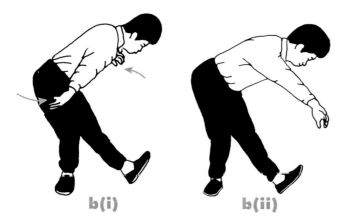

b(i)   b(ii)

c

b. Continue to swing the arms in an arc so that the left is back and the right hand forward. Hegu points should face each other and the body is still facing forward.

c. <u>Simultaneously</u>: bring the left arm up and rotate the right arm around so both palms are facing the body and are crossed to the Shanzhong point at the Middle Dantian. The Neiguan and Waiguan points on the wrists are touching each other. The arms should be relaxed and rounded, like holding a ball in front of the chest. The Laogong points in the palms should face the Qihu points on the chest. You should still be bent over slightly with all the weight resting on the right leg.

Twisting the body helps to smooth the Belt Channel and loosen the waist and joints in the arms and shoulders. When we cross the wrists, we touch the Neiguan and Waiguan points to stimulate the heart. The Laogong point of each palm facing to the Middle Dantian stimulates the Shanzhong point, again stimulating the heart and also the lungs.

13. Recover Qi

回氣

a

a. <u>Simultaneously</u>: quickly straighten the body and at the same time drop both arms down in an arc and back up to shoulder height. The upper body should be turned so facing towards the right. The palms should be open, but the feet remain in the same position. This is to help you return back to the same position in the next movement.

Swinging the arms downward in this movement releases negative Qi to the earth. We then gather fresh Qi and bring it to the Quepen point on the left side of the body. This is good for relieving stiffness in the neck and shoulder.

Quepen 缺盆

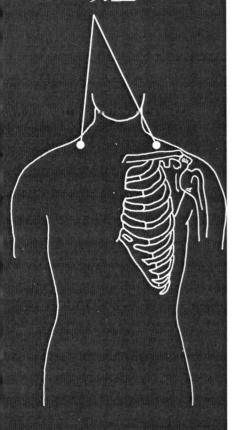

The Quepen point is located in the deep area behind the collarbone and is on the Stomach Channel.

14. Twist Left Toes

a

a. Close the five fingers of the left hand so they make a Five Finger Plum Blossom Claw. Bring the Plum Blossom Claw to the left Quepen point.

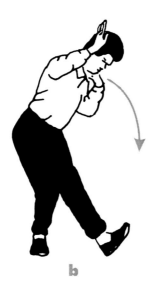

b

c

b. <u>Simultaneously</u>: swing the body to face forward again and bend down. Hold the toes of the left foot with the right hand. The thumb should be on top of the big toe and the four fingers supporting behind.

c. Using the waist, twist the toes three times, spiralling in a clock-wise direction. This movement strengthens the kidneys and loosens the waist. Although we call this movement 'Twist the Toes', actually the toes are used mostly for balance and it is the whole body that moves from the waist.

We use the toes for balance so that the movement can come from the waist. Flexibility in the waist is very important for longevity of the body. When the waist is supple, then we can walk and move without pain. You may even find that you feel lighter, like when you were a child. This is because with the waist loose, the Qi and circulation can flow more freely through both the upper and lower body.

15. Push Qi

a

a. Release the toes and push the right palm back past the right foot, turning the left heel slightly as you do so. The palm should face the earth, releasing negative Qi. All your weight should be on your right leg.

In this movement, we release negative Qi to the earth by having the Laogong point face the ground as we push the Qi backwards.

a.

b.

a. <u>Simultaneously</u>: turn the right palm and scoop Qi forwards and up, shifting the weight forward onto the left leg.

b. As the right palm comes up, close fingers into a Five Finger Plum Blossom Claw and touch the right Quepen point. The left claw is still touching the left Quepen point.

Having released negative Qi, we now gather fresh Qi and bring it back to the right Quepen point which relates to the Stomach Channel. This movement also helps to promote blood circulation and stimulation of the Quepen point is good for neck and shoulder pain.

17. Turn Body and Recover Qi

轉身回氣

a

b

a. Shift the weight backwards onto the right leg and turn on the heels 180 degrees. Turn first with the left heel and then with the right. Now the weight will be on the left leg, and you are facing the opposite direction.

b. Swing the left arm down in an arc, similar to , 'Recover Qi' (movement 13).

By turning the body, we change the direction from which to gather Qi. We turn on the heels, one at a time, to keep the Qi settled. Swinging the arm releases Qi to the earth again.

18. Twist Right Toes

右弹足

a

   a. Bend over and grasp the toes with the left hand in the same way as in, 'Twist Left Toes' (movement 14). Using the waist, twist the toes, this time in an anti-clockwise direction.

Same as movement 14.

19. Pull Qi

推
氣

a. Release the toes and push the left palm back past the
left foot, turning the right toes to follow the right hand.
Stay balanced with weight still on the left leg, and using
the right heel as a pivot as you bring the Qi back. The
palm should face the earth, releasing negative Qi.

Same as movement 15.

20. Scoop Qi

a

b

a. After bringing the Qi back, turn the left foot so it is parallel with the right foot and the body is facing forward.

b. Turn the left palm and scoop the Qi upwards until it is beneath the right elbow. The palm should be facing the body towards the liver area.

After releasing negative energy, this movement brings positive Qi to the liver.

21. Twine Hands

a

b

c

a. Lower your right hand inside the left arm. The right palm should face the spleen. The left palm should be facing the liver, the left arm on the outside of the right arm.

b. Rotate the right arm underneath the left arm. The left arm is now closest to the body. Use the waist as you move, turning the body gently from side to side.

c. Rotate the left arm underneath the right arm. The right arm is now closest to the body. During the movement, the Neiguan and Waiguan points are being stimulated by passing each other when the hands are twined.

This movement transmits Qi to the liver and spleen through the Laogong points. The liver and spleen are two of the five major internal organs in the body. The liver is related to blood and blood circulation, and the spleen is related to the stomach which is the first organ to begin processing nutrients from the foods we eat. We use the waist to gently turn the body from side to side, helping to move the Qi and to stimulate these organs even more.

a. Shift the weight to the left leg.

b

c

b. Step forward with the right foot and open the arm to the right side of the body with the palm up. The sole of the foot should open as the waist opens to the right, opening the Yongquan point. All the weight should be on the left leg.

c. When the arm reaches the side of the body, turn the palm and bring the right Hegu point to touch the right Shenshu point.

d (backview)   e(i)   e(ii)

d. At the same time as bringing the hand to the back, close the sole of the foot and shift the weight forward onto the right leg.

e. Keeping the right hand at the kidney point, step forward with the left leg and open the left arm to the left side of the body. Open the sole of the left foot as the arm sweeps open.

f

g (backview)

f. When the left arm reaches the left side of the body, turn the palm and bring the left Hegu point to touch the left Shenshu point.

g. At the same time as bringing the hand to the back, shift the weight forward onto the left leg. Both hands should now be at the Shenshu points.

h   **i**   **j (backview)**

h. Step forward with the right foot and open the right arm/right sole to the right side of the body.

i. When the arm reaches the right side of the body, turn the palm/ close the sole and bring the right Hegu to touch the right Shenshu point.

j. Shift the weight forward onto the right leg. Keep both hands at the Shenshu points.

Turning the waist smooths the Belt Channel and stimulates the kidneys. Opening the sole of the foot opens the Yongquan point allowing negative energy to release through the Kidney Channel. Bringing the Hegu point to the Shenshu point stimulates the kidney energy. This movement is good for loosening the waist and stimulating the kidneys.

23. Brush Waist

a

b

a. Step forward with the left leg, keeping the weight on the right leg and both feet flat on the ground. Brush the left hand past the belt channel and extend the arm slightly downwards and out until the left arm is extended in front of the Dantian. The palm should be facing up.

b. Extend your right arm behind you so that the Hegu point faces the Mingmen point, palm facing downwards. Now the shift weight forward onto left leg. The left leg should now be fully straight with the toes of the right foot lightly touching the ground behind the body.

淅
腰

c   c (opposite view)

c. <u>Simultaneously</u>: twist waist and swing right arm so Hegu point is facing the Sky Eye and swing the left arm so that the Hegu point is facing the Mingmen point. The right elbow should be higher than the hand so that Qi can flow downwards to Hegu point.

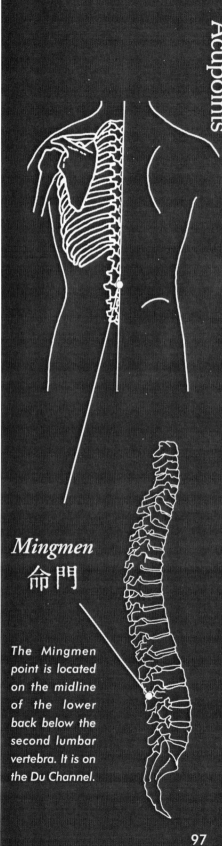

Mingmen
命門

The Mingmen point is located on the midline of the lower back below the second lumbar vertebra. It is on the Du Channel.

This movement stimulates the Mingmen point (which relates to the kidneys) and the Sky Eye. It also stimulates the Xiao Zhou Tian (Small Heavenly Circle or Microcosmic Orbit).

24. Drop Arms and Recover Qi

落膀回氣

a. Drop left arm to waist and extend right arm upwards.

b. <u>Simultaneously:</u> balancing on toes, bring the left arm up and the right arm down, rotating them like a windmill. Turn the body to the right as your arms move, still balancing on toes.

c. <u>Simultaneously:</u> when the arms begin to reach shoulder height, quickly flick Qi to the Sky Eye with the left hand and bring the right hand up to rest at the waist with the palm up. As you flick the Qi to the Sky Eye, pivot the body back to the front and drop down on the heels. The weight should be on the back leg, with the front leg straight.

The left hand stimulates the Sky Eye though the Laogong point which flicks the Qi to the Sky Eye. The right hand stimulates the Belt Channel whilst the dropping down on the heel jerks the body to help release negative Qi.

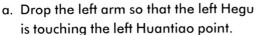

a. Drop the left arm so that the left Hegu is touching the left Huantiao point.

b. Shift weight to left leg and step forward with the right leg and open right arm as in movement 'Cloud Hands'. Note, however, that the arm should be at the level of the Sky Eye and not the waist. As the right arm opens, the eyes should watch the hand as it swings to the right. As it opens, the right Laogong point should be facing the Sky Eye. Make sure that the sole of the foot opens as the arm opens. This helps to release negative energy from the Yongquan point.

25. Spread Single Wing (cont'd)

c. When the arm reaches the side of body, shift the weight forward onto the right leg and bring back the right hand so Hegu touches right Shenshu point.

This is similar to Cloud Hands but it stimulates the Sky Eye as well as the kidneys because the hand is raised above the Sky Eye as it passes the front of the body. This movement is good for shoulder, back and neck joints.

上步伸膀

a

a. Step forward with the left leg, transferring weight to the right leg at the same time. Maintaining contact with the body, slide the left hand up from the Huantiao point to the waist and rotate the wrist outwards so that the palm is facing up. The wrist should remain in contact with the waist as it is rotating open.

The Neiguan point is stimulated as the palm rotates open at the Belt Channel.

27. Wind Hand Around Head and Ears

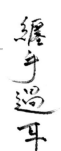

a

b

a. Lower the right hand and bring it around the front of the body to the finger tips of the left palm.

b. Continue to pass the palm on the outside of the left palm, up outside of the arm, up to the left Taiyang point, past the Fengchi, Fengfu and Yuzhen points on the back of head and past the right Taiyang point. Your eyes should watch the right hand as it smooths Qi past the left arm. Weight should be on the right leg.

There are many acupuncture points around the temples and back of head that relate to the Opening the Heaven Gate. Some of the main ones are Taiyang, (located at the temple) and Fengfu, Fengchi and Yuzhen. We smooth the Qi with the Laogong point, helping to balance the Qi in the upper and lower body.

28. Press Qi Down

下壓

a

a. <u>Simultaneously</u>: when the right palm reaches the right Taiyang point, lower the right arm (palm down) and lift the left arm up (palm up). Lower the right arm until the right Hegu point faces the right Huantiao point. The left arm should be at shoulder height. Look at the left hand as it rises.

This movement prepares the body for gathering and releasing Qi. We lean slightly forwards, with the weight on the front leg, to help the body gather Qi for the next movement. In this movement one hand is down, connecting with the Earth Qi and the other is up, connecting with the Heaven Qi.

Fengfu 風府

This point is located one thumb's width above the hairline in the depression in the centre of the back of the neck on the Du Channel.

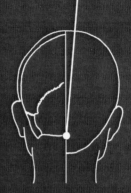

Yuzhen 玉枕

This is located on the back of the head, where the two bones come up, and is where your head rests on your pillow when you sleep. It is on the Urinary Bladder Channel.

Fengchi 風池

This point is found below the nape of the neck in the depressions on either side of the occipital bone. Fengchi is on the Gall Bladder Channel.

上
托

a

a. Turn both palms, left palm facing down and right palm
facing upwards. Shift the weight forward onto the left
leg, knee straight, slightly lean the body forward as
well. Raise the right arm and lower the left arm.

*In this movement also, one hand is down, connecting with the Earth Qi and the other
is up, connecting with the Heaven Qi but on the opposite sides of the body from the
previous movement.*

30. Recover Qi

a

b

a. <u>Simultaneously</u>: stand on toes, close right fingers into a Five Finger Plum Blossom Claw and turn the body to the right.

b. <u>Simultaneously</u>: drop the Five Finger Plum Blossom Claw to the Quepen point and bring the left arm up to flick Qi to the Sky Eye and drop down on the heels, turning the body to face forward as you do so. When you flick Qi to the Sky Eye, the wrist is loose and the body relaxed. You should flick the Qi and drop down on the heels at the same time, thus, stimulating the Sky Eye and releasing negative energy through the Yongquan points.

This stimulates the Sky Eye and helps open our human potential. When we flick the Qi with the left hand, we should make sure that the hand is slightly above the Yintang point so that we are looking at the Laogong point with the chin lifted, not looking down. At the same time, the right fingers are closed, focusing all the Qi in the fingertips so that when they touch the Quepen point, the Qi is transmitted to the Stomach Channel.

31. Scoop the Moon

a.

b.

a. Keep the left hand in the same position as at end of last movement. Turn the waist to the right and extend the right palm up from the Quepen point. Open the fingers and to collect Qi from the sky, watching the right hand.

b. Bend from the waist and scoop the right hand downwards, watching the right palm the entire time.

c

c (sideview)

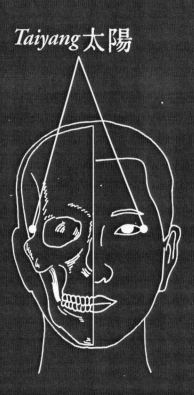

Taiyang 太陽

c. Bring the palm downwards in an arc until the wrists meet. Turn the head and look to the left. The right Laogong point should face the Sky Eye. The left Laogong point should face right Taiyang point. Keep the arms hollowed like holding a ball and do not collapse the chest. The waist should be bent no further than 90 degrees. All your weight should be on the right leg.

Taiyang means pupil crevice and is one of the strong acupuncture points. It is located one inch to the side of our eyes and is one of the extra-ordinary points not belonging to any of the regular channels.

This movement works with the whole body to scoop Qi and then transmit it through the Laogong point to the Sky Eye. This movement is good for settling Qi and balancing the mind.

32. Turn Body

a.　b.　c.

a. Keep your hands in the same position and turn on the heels 180 degrees. Begin turning with the left heel and then turn on the right heel, one at a time. This way the transition will be smooth and the Qi will remain settled. Weight should now be on the left leg.

b. Turn the left palm inwards and bring the Hegu down to touch the left Huantiao point. Eyes should look at the right palm.

c. Straighten the body, moving the weight forward onto the right leg, knee bent. Keep the right Laogong point facing the Sky Eye as you straighten the body.

We touch the Hegu point of the left hand to the Huantiao point so the Qi can go down the Huantiao point to the Yongquan point. When we bring the Qi to the Sky Eye, this helps open the channels in the head so that the Qi can flow better. By increasing the flow of blood and Qi, the brain is nourished more and is more healthy. That is why some people say that Qigong can make you smarter.

33. Step Forward and Look at Palm

a. Shift the arm to the right so that the right Laogong point now faces the right Taiyang point. However, you still remain with eyes looking forwards.

b. <u>Simultaneously</u>: step forward with the left leg, weight on the right leg and bring the left palm up to face the Sky Eye.

The Qi passes through the head, clearing blockages, helping headaches and possibly improving eyesight.

34. Look at the Moon

a

b

c

a. Keep the left hand in the same position as at the end of the last move-ment. Turn the waist to the right and extend the right palm up from the Taiyang point, watching the hand all the time. Open the fingers and palm to collect Qi from the sky.

b. Bend from the waist and scoop the right hand downwards, watching the right palm the entire time.

c. Bring the palm downwards in an arc until it is facing straight down to the ground, elbows of the arms just at the point of crossing. At this point quickly bend the right elbow and flick Qi to the Sky Eye, looking to the left as you do so. This should bring you to the same position as in 'Scoop the Moon' (movement 31).

This movement is the same as 'Scoop the Moon' (movement 31) but in this movement, the Qi is flicked quickly when the lower arm is vertical to the ground, rather than bringing the Qi up to the Sky Eye in a smooth transition. This flicking movement transmits a quick jolt of Qi to the Sky Eye to help open this area.

a.　Turn the body to face forward in the same direction as the feet.

b.　Open elbows outwards and squat down, simultaneously pressing both palms down either side of the left leg. The Laogong points should face the earth. When we press down we count this as one.

c.　Stand up slightly with palms at knee level and press down a further two times. When standing up during this set of movements, do not stand up all the way. Instead, keep the body slightly bent when pressing up and down and bring the hands no higher then knee level.

When you move up and down with the palms facing the ankles, the Laogong points transmit energy to the earth and help to open the three Yin and three Yang channels in the foot. The up and down movement also is for arthritis and for making the legs and ankles stronger. When the legs are stronger, the kidneys, back and bones will all be stronger.

36. Turn the Body and Press Qi

a

b

c

a. Raise up the body until standing straight, arms at the sides.

b. Turn the right foot outwards 90 degrees and adjust the left foot slightly to balance the weight for the squatting down movements to come. Open elbows outwards and squat down, simultaneously pressing both palms down either side of the right leg. The Laogong points should face the earth. This pressing down is one count.

c. Stand up slightly with palms at knee level and press down a further two times. When standing up during this set of movements, do not stand up all the way. Instead, keep the body slightly bent when pressing up and down and bring the hands no higher then knee level.

In this movement, it is important to make sure that you turn only 90 degrees. This turning means you have now covered a third direction in the Dayan Qigong form. Each direction relates to one of the cardinal points of the compass. These four directions plus centre (yourself) relate to the principle of the Five Elements.

a   b   c

a. While still kneeling, shift the weight back onto the left leg.

b. While still kneeling begin to flutter the hands up to shoulder level. When you reach shoulder height raise the body slowly upwards, keeping the weight wholly on the left leg, while at the same time fluttering the hands. Look up as your hands flutter upwards.

c. Flutter the hands until fully standing and arms are above head, Hegu points facing Taiyang points, weight on the back leg.

Fluttering of the hands stimulates the internal organs and releases negative energy. This is a special movement in the Dayan Qigong forms. As the hands flutter up and down, this also smooths the channels throughout the body. Raising from a squatting position to a standing one brings the Qi up to the face and head, enabling you to gather more energy from heaven and smooth the Ren and Du channels.

38. Look Down at Water

a   b   c

a. While continuing to flutter hands, open arms down and out to the sides until level with your shoulders.

b. Shift the weight forward onto the right leg and keep the knee straight. The left foot should balance the body, toes loosely touching the ground, behind the body.

c. Keep fluttering the hands and bring the palms back so that the Laogong points of both hands face the Shenshu points from a distance of around 12-14 inches. The chest and Qihu points should be open and eyes looking straight ahead.

The Laogong points transmit energy to the kidneys as they face the Shenshu points. Looking forward and opening the chest helps release excess Qi through the Qihu points and through the eyes.

39. Pat Water and Fly Away

拍
水
飛
翔

a

b

a. Continue to flutter hands and bring arms forward to shoulder level on the right side of the body. The arms should be rounded like a circle. The fingers of the left hand should point to the Hegu point of the right hand. The back foot can adjust so moving from side to side is comfortable.

b. <u>Simultaneously</u>: shift the weight to the left side and flutter hands past the Dantian and up to the left side, to shoulder level. The fingers of the right hand should point to the Hegu point of the left hand. When doing this movement, the action should be smooth and continuous.

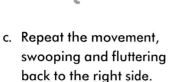

c. Repeat the movement, swooping and fluttering back to the right side.

d. Repeat the movement, swooping and fluttering back to the left side.

e. <u>Simultaneously</u>: shift body so facing forwards and flutter hands to the front so that the Hegu points are facing the Qihu points.

This movement should be gentle and smooth. Your weight and your hands should both swing in unison and the attitude should be that of a flying bird. Moving the waist and fluttering the hands releases the poisons in the body and smooths the channels and creates relaxation.

40. Drink Water

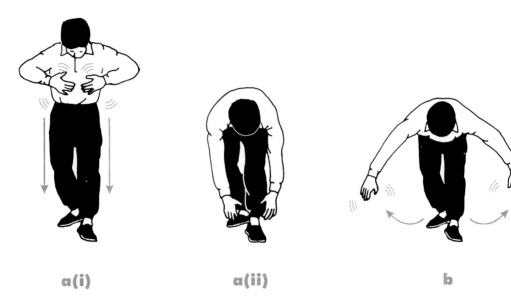

a(i)   a(ii)   b

a. <u>Simultaneously</u>: still fluttering hands, step forward with your left leg, keeping weight on the right leg. Flutter hands down the front of the body and down past either side of the left leg to the ankle. This is like washing the body.

b. Flutter the hands out to either side of the leg in a movement like a half circle, fluttering up to pass the liver and spleen.

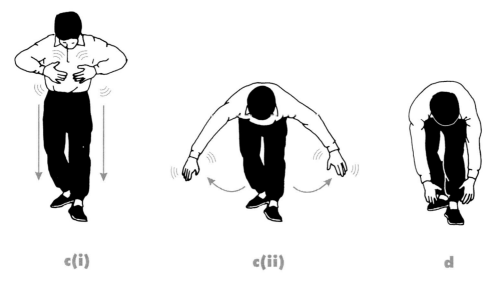

c(i)   c(ii)   d

c. Wash down the body again and come back up to the liver and spleen.

d. Wash down the body again but this time flutter only as far as the ankle.

When doing this movement, make sure that your palms pass over your liver and spleen, helping to nourish these organs. This movement stimulates the three Yin and three Yang channels of the leg as the hands pass down. This also helps the body release negative energy and helps Qi flow. Bending from the waist and balancing the weight on the back leg helps strengthen the kidneys.

a

a. <u>Simultaneously</u>: still fluttering hands, shift the weight
   forward onto the left leg (knee straight) and raise the arms
   upwards, fluttering hands the entire time. When hands are
   above the head, stop fluttering and look up. The elbows
   should be slightly rounded.

*The previous movements help release ill and stagnant Qi from the body. Now we
need to collect fresh Qi to replace it. This movement concentrates the energy at the
upper Dantian and collects Qi through the Laogong points and transmits Qi to the
Taiyang points through the Hegu points.*

a. Bring right leg forward so both feet are parallel. Lower hands to the Dantian.

b. Place hands on either side of the Dantian, the right hand being slightly lower than the left hand. The hands should be just a few inches on either side of the Dantian and should be hollowed, like arched bridges.

c. Quiver the hands quickly up and down three times, with a pause of 2-3 seconds of stillness in between each quiver. When quivering the fingers, make sure that they do not move from their position. The purpose is to stimulate the Dantian.

In the previous movement, 'Gaze at the Sky' (movement 41), we create a lot of Qi in the upper Dantian. We now want to collect the Qi and bring it to the Lower Dantian. The left hand is slightly higher than the right hand and covers the spleen. The right hand is slightly lower and covers the liver. The higher hand is the one to transmit the most energy. Therefore, if you have a liver problem, then you can change the hands around, so the right hand is higher than the left.

43. Grasp Qi

a

b

c

a. Reach forward with the right hand and grasp Qi.

b. Close the hand and bring Qi back so that right Hegu point faces right Qihu point. The arm should be horizontal, with the elbow not higher than the shoulder.

c. Repeat movement with the left hand, bringing back to left Qihu point. Repeat the movement a further four times on each side, for a total of ten times, five times on each side.

The Qihu points act as doors for the Qi to enter the body. Having collected the Qi, we then bring it into the Qihu points. This helps stimulate the lungs and is good for asthma and bronchitis. The Qihu points are located on the Stomach Channel.

Houxi 後谿

This point is located on the outer edge of the palm at the junction of the white and red skin. It is on the Small Intestine Channel.

44. Turn Palm Up and Gather Qi

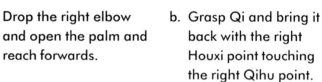

a. Drop the right elbow and open the palm and reach forwards.

b. Grasp Qi and bring it back with the right Houxi point touching the right Qihu point.

c(i)

c(ii)

c(iv)

c. Grasp Qi with the left palm and bring back so that the left Houxi point touches the left Qihu point.

d. Repeat on either side a further four times on each side, for a total of ten times, five times on each side.

This movement is similar to the previous movement, but instead of transmitting Qi with the Hegu points, we now do so with the Houxi points.

45. Hold the Ball

抱球

a. Open hands with palms facing each other like holding a ball and raise the ball up to the Sky Eye. Then open arms out to the sides of the body as if still holding a Qi ball.

b. When hands reach the shoulders, bend forward from the waist, keeping legs straight and the arms extended on either side of the body as if still holding a very large Qi ball. Elbows should be slightly bent.

Having opened the Qihu points, the Qi becomes strong. Holding the Qi in the hands benefits the other organs as each finger relates to one of the five major internal organs.

46. Rotate the Qi Ball

探球

a. Straighten the body and bring the Qi ball to the left waist. The right hand should be on top and the left hand underneath, Laogong points facing each other. The weight of the body should be on the right side.

b. Rotate the ball by moving the bottom hand in an anti-clockwise circle and moving the top hand in a anti-clockwise circle ten times, from the left waist to the right waist. At the same time, the waist should move in unison with the hands, transferring the weight smoothly from the left to right side of the body. When rotating the ball, the fingers should move to help stimulate each of the five major internal organs.

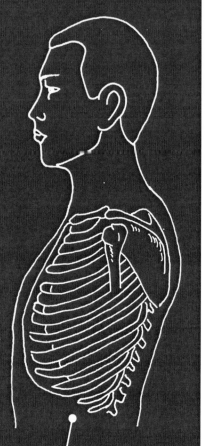

Daimai 帶脈

This point is found on the same level as the navel and is directly below the eleventh rib. This point is on the Gall Bladder Channel.

46. Rotate the Qi Ball (cont'd)

c. On the tenth rotation, you should have reached the right waist and the weight should be on the left side of the body.

This movement releases negative Qi with the bottom hand which is moving outwards and gathers positive Qi with the upper hand which is moving inwards. The movement also stimulates the liver and spleen and helps smooth Qi along the Belt Channel and brings energy to the Daimai points.

47. Turn the Body and Rotate the Qi Ball

a

b

c

a. Turn the palms so left hand is now on top and facing the right hand. The weight of the body should now be on the left side.

b. Repeat the previous movement, shifting the weight slowly and smoothly from left to right as you rotate the ball. However, this time we only rotate the ball seven times to reach the left waist. Both hands now move in a clockwise circle.

c. On the seventh rotation, keeping the hands in the same position and without changing the direction of the rotating hands, rotate the ball three more times from left to right, until the hands are at the Dantian. The weight should now be at the centre of the body and placed evenly on both feet.

This movement has the same effect as in the previous movement but ends with bringing Qi back to the Dantian.

48. Hold Qi

a. Lift up the Qi ball so that it is just above your Sky Eye.

b. Separate the hands and then open out to sides.

c. Bend forward at the waist while holding a large Qi ball. Keep the knees straight. The elbows should be slightly bent and body relaxed.

d. Shake your shoulders letting the Qi ripple down the arms to the hands.

e. Still holding the Qi ball, squat down.

First, we gather the Qi and bring it to the Sky Eye. Then we open the arms, while holding onto a large Qi ball. When we shake the upper body, while still holding the Qi ball, loosen the shoulders, back and waist. When these are loose, the Qi can flow more strongly down to the hands in preparation for the next movement. Facing the palms towards each other means we gather even more energy through the Laogong points.

49. Pour Qi

a

b

a. Slowly lift up the Qi ball to shoulder height while still squatting. Imagine that the Qi ball is very heavy.

b. Continue to stand up all the way, lifting the Qi ball slowly upwards. As you stand up hold the Qi ball slightly forwards and out from the body.

c

d

c. Turn palms and pour the Qi to the Sky Eye by bringing the palms towards it slowly.

d. Continue to lower hands very slowly down the front of the body, past the Middle Dantian and to the Lower Dantian. Let hands remain at the Dantian for three seconds, Laogong points facing the Dantian.

This movement lets the Qi penetrate down from the Sky Eye to the Middle Dantian and then to the Lower Dantian. This helps to develop the Dan.

50. Raise Wings

a. Relax and lower the arms to the side of the body.

b. <u>Simultaneously</u>: gather Qi from either side of the body and raise your hands outwards and upwards to face the Sky Eye while coming up onto the balls of your feet.

c

d

c. Bring your hands and Qi to the Sky Eye until about three inches away.

d. <u>Simultaneously:</u> quickly turn the palms outwards and push the Qi from the Sky Eye and at the same time, drop your heels to the ground, bending the knees slightly. The hands should be slightly higher than the Sky Eye and the knees should be bent. Eyes should be looking up at the hands.

After the three Dantians have been stimulated (upper, middle and lower), we then bring the Qi up to the Sky Eye and quickly release it. Dropping onto the heels at the same time helps further release Qi through the Yongquan points.

51. Drop Wings

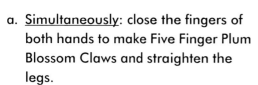

a

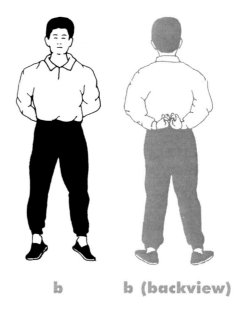

b   b (backview)

a. <u>Simultaneously</u>: close the fingers of both hands to make Five Finger Plum Blossom Claws and straighten the legs.

b. Bring the claws back so the Hegu and Shenshu points touch.

Closing the hands into Five Finger Plum Blossom Claws, helps gather more Qi which we then transmit to the Shenshu points by connecting with the Hegu points.

52. Bring Wings to the Back

a

b

a. Let the fingers relax but still keep the Hegu points in contact with the Shenshu points. Quickly quiver the Hegu points up and down three times and then pause for 2-3 seconds.

b. Repeat the quivering and pausing a further two times.

We rub the Hegu points against the Shenshu points to strengthen the kidneys. This is a good movement for backache. If you have backache or stiffness, this movement can even be done as a single exercise to help relieve pain in the lower back.

53. Fly Up to the Side

a
b

Tiantu
天突

This point is located on the neck in the centre of the suprasternal fossa and is on the Ren Channel.

a. Bring both hands forward in front of the body to shoulder level. Hands should still be in Five Finger Plum Blossom Claws. The claws should be side by side, but not touching, shoulder width apart.

b. Relax the wrists and open the hands and lower the arms, folding the right hand over the left. The hands should be in front of the Dantian with a space of a few inches between both hands and the Dantian.

c.   Shift the weight to the right side and step forward with the left foot, keeping all the weight on the right leg. Raise the left hand up palm facing the Ren Channel, to the Tiantu point.

d.   <u>Simultaneously</u>: turn the waist to the left so that the hand also moves to the left, following the body. At the same time, open the sole of the foot to release negative energy from the Yongquan point. As the hand follows the waist, it should come up to Sky Eye level. Keep the elbows open and the Laogong point facing the Sky Eye.

e.   <u>Simultaneously</u>: close the sole of the foot and shift the weight forward on the left leg, knee bent.

53. Fly Up to the Side (cont'd)

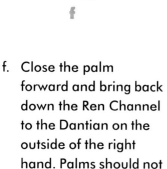

f.

g.

h.

f. Close the palm forward and bring back down the Ren Channel to the Dantian on the outside of the right hand. Palms should not touch.

g. Repeat the same movement for a total of seven times, alternating left and right and ending with the left leg forward.

h. On the seventh step, step forward with the left foot and bring the palm up to the Tiantu point. Turn the waist to the left so that the hand follows and open the sole of the foot. Stop here and do not close as before.

This movement should be repeated for a total of seven times. Seven is a special Daoist number which relates to the constellation The Big Dipper. When we move the hand up and then back down, we exchange Qi from the Dantian and Sky Eye. This helps to smooth the Ren Channel. Opening the sole of the foot helps to release negative Qi from the Yongquan point.

a

b

a. Bring both hands to the Dantian by fluttering.

b. Turn to the opposite direction 180 degrees, first on the left heel and then on the right heel. Keep fluttering as you turn and keep the hands at the Dantian. Stop fluttering when you have completed the turn and keep the hands at the Dantian.

Turning on the heels helps us to develop our centre of gravity. So when we turn, we should do so one heel at a time, smoothly without losing balance. Changing direction helps us to cover all four directions of the compass:- north, south, east and west. Covering the four directions also relates to the Five Elements, with our body being the Centre and relating to the element Earth.

55. Fly Upward

a

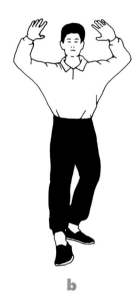

b

a. Slowly raise the arms so that palms are facing up. Keep the elbows rounded slightly.

b. Look up, keeping weight on the left leg, the front leg light. The Hegu points should be facing the Taiyang points.

This posture gathers Heaven Qi from the sky through the Laogong points and then transmits to the Sky Eye through the Hegu points. As the hands raise, we gather Qi in the palms.

56. Skim over the Sea

a. Step forward with the left leg, keeping weight on the right leg.

b. Begin to flutter hands while turning the waist 45 degrees behind, so that you are looking slightly backwards. The arms should be in a loose circle with the fingers of the left hand pointing to the Hegu point of the right hand.

c (i)   c (ii)

c. <u>Simultaneously</u>: still fluttering, drop the hands and
    bend the waist and in a swooping movement flutter
    hands past the ankle.

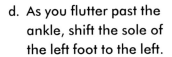

d. As you flutter past the ankle, shift the sole of the left foot to the left.

e. While continuing to flutter, continue the swooping movement upwards to the left and move the weight forward onto the left leg. The left leg should be straight and the arms should now be in a loose circle on the left side of the body with the fingers of the right hand pointing to the Hegu point of the left hand.

56. Skim over the Sea (cont'd)

f(i)

f(ii)

g

f. Step forward with the right leg, keeping the weight on the left leg. Repeat the movement but on the right side.

g. Repeat again, alternating on both sides for a total of seven times, however, on the last movement, do not shift your foot and keep body slightly bent at the waist.

This movement is quite similar to 'Pat Water and Fly Away' (movement 39), except in this you are walking forwards. This movement is good for the waist, back and kidneys. We gather Qi to the Middle Dantian by keeping the arms in a circle as we flutter. The fingers of one hand point to the Hegu point of the other.

a. Begin to flutter both hands and flutter them to the Dantian. While still fluttering, turn first on the left heel and then on the right heel until you have turned the body 180 degrees. Stop fluttering.

Same as in movement 54.

58. Fly Upward

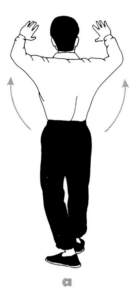

a. Slowly raise the arms so that palms are facing up,
    Hegu points facing Taiyang points. Look up,
    keeping weight on the back leg.

Same as in 'Fly Upward' (movement 55).

寻
食

a

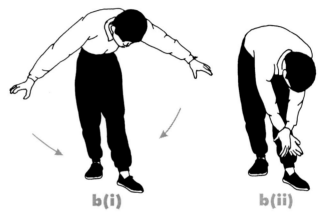

b(i)   b(ii)

a. Step forward with the
left foot and open arms
to the sides of the body
shoulder level.

b. Keeping weight on the rear leg, bend forward at
the waist and allow arms to swoop down so that
they cross at the ankles. Let them continue their
momentum and bring back up to the thigh, palms
facing the leg.

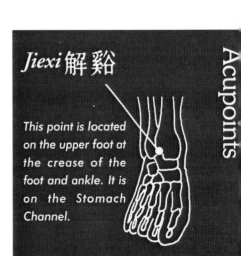

Jiexi 解豀

*This point is located
on the upper foot at
the crease of the
foot and ankle. It is
on the Stomach
Channel.*

Acupoints

59. Look for Food (cont'd)

b(iii)

c(i)

c(ii)

b. Continuation of previous movement.

c. Open elbows and smooth Qi down the leg, palms facing the leg and fingers facing each other, but not touching.

d. When hands reach the ankles, raise your body and open your hands out to your sides again. As you do this, your weight will shift forward onto the left leg.

e. Step forward with the right leg and repeat the movement for a total of seven times.

59. Look for Food (cont'd)

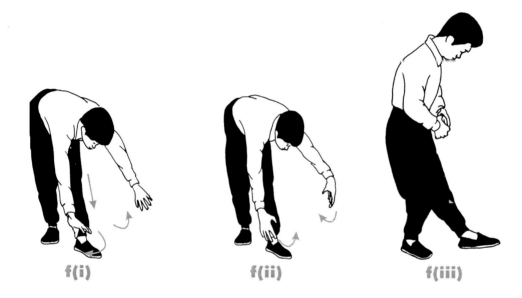

f(i)   f(ii)   f(iii)

f. On the seventh step, having smoothed Qi down the left leg to the ankle, open the palms outward and push forward, then turn the palms to gather a Qi ball. Bring the Qi ball back in to the ankle and up the leg to the Dantian.

As you perform the swooping movements, you should keep your back and waist relaxed. You should then find that your back moves in a natural wave-like manner. This movement is very good for the spine and helps maintain the flexibility of the back and waist so that Qi can flow smoothly around the Belt Channel. This movement also smoothes the Stomach Channel on the leg. On the seventh time, we gather Qi and bring it back to the Dantian in preparation for the next movement. This movement and that of Flying Up to the Sides and Skimming Over the Sea are quite dynamic movements. These strong movements help to balance the earlier movements which are more static.

a.

a. Turn first on the left heel and then on the right heel
   180 degrees. Hands should still be at the Dantian.

This movement is similar to, 'Turn Body' (movement 54), however, we do not flutter the hands upwards. Instead, we keep them at the Dantian in preparation for the next movement as we turn 180 degrees.

61. Look for the Nest

a

b (sideview)

c

a. Raise hands to the Middle Dantian, with fingers and wrists completely relaxed.

b. Step forward with the left foot, and at the same time, press the palms down on the left side of the body until level with the Belt Channel.

c. Step forward with the right foot, lift the hands to the Middle Dantian.

d (sideview)   **e**   **f (sideview)**

d. Press hands down to the Lower Dantian.

e. Step forward with the left foot, lift the hands to the Middle Dantian.

f. Press the palms down on the right side of the body until level with the Belt Channel.

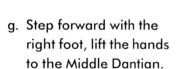

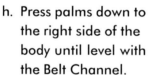

g. Step forward with the right foot, lift the hands to the Middle Dantian.

h. Press palms down to the right side of the body until level with the Belt Channel.

i. Step forward with the left foot, lift the hands to the Middle Dantian.

j (sideview)   k   l (sideview)

j. Press palms down to the Lower Dantian.

k. Step forward with the right foot, lift the hands to the Middle Dantian.

l. Press the palms down to the left side of the body one more time.

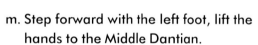

m

n (sideview)

m. Step forward with the left foot, lift the hands to the Middle Dantian.

n. Press palms down to the Lower Dantian.

This movement again has seven steps. With each step we press down the palms:- left, centre, right, right, centre, left and centre again. This concentrates all the Qi around the Belt Channel, opening it so that negative energy can pass down to the Yongquan point. Each time you lift the foot you take in good Qi and when you press down, you release negative Qi. This movement imitates the movement of a wild goose building its nest.

62. Turn Body and Swim

a (sideview)   a   b

a. <u>Simultaneously</u>: pivot on the heel and open the left foot 90 degrees to the left. At the same time, begin to flutter hands from the Dantian up to the sides of the body to shoulder level.

b. As the arms get just to shoulder height, step forward with the right foot so it is parallel with the left. Look forward. You should now be three steps in front of the original starting position from where you began the form. If not, then your stepping or turning must be off and so you should check yourself next time.

c. Still fluttering, bring arms together so they are shoulder width apart in front of the body.

d. Lower the hands while still fluttering and touch the tips of the fingers to the Dantian.

Turning the body 90 degrees brings us back so that we are in our original starting position. We have now covered all four directions (north, south, east and west) in the form. If you find you do not end three steps in front of where you started, then you will need to check that you are walking the correct number of steps or turning correctly during the form.

63. Sleep Peacefully and Recover Qi

a

a. Bend forward from the waist and squat down, still touching the fingers to the Dantian. Slightly tuck in your chin so that the Sky Eye faces the Dantian and shut the eyes and keep the mouth closed. Hold this posture for ten seconds.

This movement recovers Qi and brings it to the Dantian. We bend over and squat so that the Sky Eye connects and concentrates all the energy at the Dantian. The finger tips should be below the Qihai point and the thumbs above.

64. Shou Gong

a. Lift up your head and open your eyes.

b. Slowly stand up with knees relaxed but straight.

c(i)   c(ii)   d

c. Slowly raise the hands out to the sides of the body to shoulder level, then bring the palms to the Sky Eye.

d. Lower the palms, which should be facing the body, past the face, past the Middle Dantian and to the Lower Dantian. Repeat this movement a further two times.

This is the ending movement which brings the Qi back to the Dantian.

Meditation

Balancing Yin and Yang : Meditation

After we finish practising, we need to do meditation. Movement is the Yang side of our Qigong practice and meditation is the Yin side. Everything in nature has both a Yin and Yang side, a balance of opposites. Many of you will be familiar with what is often referred to as the Taiji symbol. Actually this shows us how, within the Yang portion (white) of the symbol, there is some Yin. Man is associated with Yang. In the black area, we see there is a small dot of white, showing that there is also Yang within the Yin. Ladies are associated with Yin.

We can also see from the merging symbol that when it comes to its fullest point, that it changes and becomes opposite. If you have ever filled a cup to overflowing, you will see that when the water spills over, it does not stop when it is level with the rim. Instead, more flows out and so it is less than full at the end. So everything in nature, when it comes to the fullest point, will change to its opposite. If we understand this and what role the Five Elements play in our emotions, then we can understand human nature better and we can know how to behave in society with less conflict.

When we do meditation, we gather Qi and store it in the area of the body we call the Dantian. "Dan" means crystal and "Tian" means heaven. If we do not store the energy in this area, then we will not be able to use the Qi later, when the body needs it. I know for many people meditation is even more difficult than doing the movements because they find it difficult to quiet the mind, be still and relax. Neglecting meditation, however, will mean that you will not be able to develop a very high Qigong level. We should develop both the mind and body in Qigong. Without both, we will not have balance.

One way to relax the mind can be to listen to your breath as it moves in and out of your body. Some others may find it useful to listen to a guided meditation, like the kind that I do in my classes. For those who prefer to have a guided meditation, I have made an audio meditation tape so that people can practise along with it. This will help you develop the habit of meditation and relaxation.

Another way to relax is to lightly focus the mind at the Dantian. Every time you feel the mind wander, bring its attention back to this area. For more details on how to do meditation, you can refer to the Meditation chapter. This will give you step by step instructions for three different methods of Qigong meditation.

How to do Meditation

The Kunlun Dayan Qigong system has many methods of meditation but they are all based upon either sitting, standing or lying down. In any one of these methods, there are a few principles which we should follow to get the best health results.

Breathing

One of the principles of meditation relates to breathing. We always breathe in through the nose and also breathe out through the nose. The nose is the body's natural filtering system. When we practise, the breath warms and the nasal passage is lubricated so that it can perform its function more efficiently. Breathing through the nose also brings the breath to the Dantian. In this way there is no need to try and guide the breath to be deeper or expand the abdomen. It will happen naturally.

Hand Position

The blood and Qi flow differently in the body for men and women. In a man, the Qi will move in a clockwise direction, whereas in a lady, it moves in an anti-clockwise direction. Therefore, when we place the hands at the Dantian, the man's left hand is against the Dantian and for ladies, it is the right hand which should be against the Dantian. If the hands are open, and lying at the Dantian, then for men, the left will be on top and for ladies, the right hand will be on top. This never changes as placing them in this way creates Yang energy for men and Yin energy for ladies.

Once, one of my students asked me about the Shaolin Monks. He had seen a picture where the men were meditating with the right hand on top, hence creating Yin energy. Why is this? The Shaolin forms create a lot of heat in the body and too much fire can be as bad as too much cold. Therefore, they do meditation in this way to help release the heat from the body.

Types of Meditation

There are many different types of meditation in the Kunlun Dayan system. In these pages, we will introduce some basic meditation postures which are easy and enjoyable to do.

Sitting Meditation

This is one of the most common forms of meditation.

We begin by sitting forward on the edge of a chair. We do this so that the Qi can flow around all of the body. The posture should be straight, with the Baihui point and Huiyin point in a straight line. Do not let the head drop during meditation.

Place the feet shoulder width apart, with the front of the knees in line with the tips of the toes.

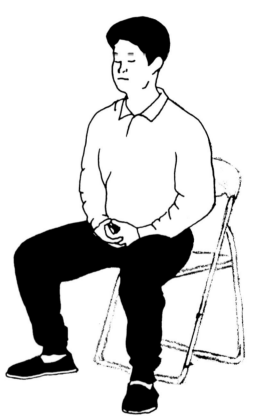

Lay the palms one on top of the other (as appropriate for man or woman) in front of the Dantian on the lap. Touch the tips of the thumbs together, connecting the two sides of the body together.

Touch the tip of the tongue to the upper palate and close the mouth. This will help connect the upper and lower channels. Close the eyes and breathe naturally through the nose.

Start with five minutes and slowly build up to a longer period. To finish meditation, do Shou Gong.

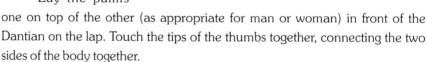

Shou Gong

Shou means collecting or harvesting. Gong means work. At the end of the meditation, we rub the palms together to make them warm. We then rub past the eyes, top and back of head, ears, mouth and nose. We rub the face three times.

Now drop the hands to your sides and collect the Qi to the Dantian three times. Shou Gong is the same movement we do at the end of the form, when we have finished practice.

Standing Meditation

Standing meditation helps develop leg strength and makes the kidneys stronger. Kidneys are also related to our bones and marrow. It is good to alternate and do both sitting and standing meditations. If you are more tired, then you can do a sitting meditation.

Stand with the feet shoulder width apart, knees slightly bent. Place the hands so the palms are facing the Dantian, elbows slightly rounded, at a distance of about 10-15 centimetres away (6-8 inches).

Make sure that all the weight is on the thighs and the hips are not tilting forwards. The Baihui and Huiyin points should be in line.

Touch the tip of the tongue to the upper palate and close the mouth. This will help connect the upper and lower channels. Close the eyes and breathe naturally through the nose.

Do not let the body sway. If you find you are moving, then sink down slightly, so more weight is on the thighs. We want to control the Qi and not let the Qi control us. That is why we do not want to let the body move around in meditation.

Start with five minutes and slowly build up to a longer period. To finish meditation, do Shou Gong.

Shou Gong

Open the eyes and straighten the legs. Rub the palms together to make them warm. Rub past the eyes, top and back of head, ears, mouth and nose. We do this rubbing of the face three times.

Now drop the hands to your sides and collect the Qi to the Dantian three times. Shou Gong is the same movement we do at the end of the form, when we have finished practice.

Lying Meditation

I do not usually recommend lying meditation. Do you know why? If you have ever tried it, then maybe you know the answer... it is very easy to fall asleep! However, for people who are very ill, this type of meditation can be helpful and will not take a lot of energy.

Do not lie on the floor or ground to do this meditation. Earth takes our energy so we want to be above the ground. It is best to lie on a bed so that the Qi can flow around you.

Lie on your back with your palms crossed over each other at the Dantian. For men, place the left hand against the Dantian first and the right hand over the top. For ladies, place the right hand against the Dantian and the left hand over the top.

Touch the tip of the tongue to the upper palate and close the mouth. This will help connect the upper and lower channels. Close the eyes and breathe naturally through the nose.

Start with five minutes and slowly build up to a longer period. To finish meditation, do Shou Gong.

Shou Gong

Open the eyes and sit up. Rub the palms together to make them warm. Rub past the eyes, top and back of head, ears, mouth and nose. Rub the face three times.

Now drop the hands to your sides and collect the Qi to the Dantian three times. Shou Gong is the same movement we do at the end of the form, when we have finished practice.

Chapter 6

Wild Goose Qigong
Practitioners

Letters

Traditional Skill

I first came across Michael Tse in an advert in my local paper. It talked about how Sifu had come over from Hong Kong and developed his own exercises. When I read this I lost interest because I was looking for "traditional" Chinese martial arts (how easy it is to be misled). However, a few months after that I came across another advert, this time for Taijiquan, so I decided to have a look. Actually, I had already been practising Yang style for ten months, so I went to the new class with an, "I'm quite good" attitude, only to be knocked down to earth by the complexity and difficulty of Chen Family Taijiquan. That first lesson was an eye-opener, and the spiralling nature of Chen had me hooked. Although intrigued by the Chen movements, the difficulty of it caused me to give up for brief periods, but I always went back for more (eventually).

There are perhaps three reasons why I started to learn Qigong from Sifu Tse. In 1995 I began to think that I was missing out on something. Sifu's teachings had begun to make me realise that Taijiquan could not be looked upon as an isolated art, but as something that is inextricably linked in the vast cauldron that is Chinese culture. Also, most of the seniors were also practising Qigong and benefiting from it. Later on in the year I went to Hong Kong and China on business. I expected to see lots of Taijiquan but found very little. Almost everybody I saw was practising some form of Qigong, especially around the trees. Also, it was about this time that I saw the seniors practising the Shaolin Damo Staff. It was something that I wanted to learn, but I knew that I would have to start at the beginning, with Dayan Qigong. So the rest is history, except for the fact that I originally had no idea just how much I would grow to respect Qigong.

The 1st 64 remains one of my favourite forms, both for its movements and feeling. Before I started Qigong, my health was not particularly good. I was forever having colds or flu, was always very pale and I used to get sore skin on the top of my hands. Dayan Qigong has improved my health considerably. I very rarely get colds, and provided I keep practising, I don't suffer with my hands any more. Qigong has also helped me to maintain my flexibility and improve my co-ordination and balance, of which co-ordination was previously virtually non-existent.

Rick Charles,
Bedford, England

Wild Goose Helps Circulation

I find that practising Dayan Qigong helps to keep my body flexible, all my joints and ligaments are very gently stretched. I also find it good for my circulation and I am always warm after practice even when it is cold and damp outside. I remember when I first started practising I did not feel anything in particular but this did not discourage me. What is important is frequent practice, any feelings or sensations will come naturally.

Chi Man Tang
London, England

On Wild Goose Qigong

When I first started the Wild Goose Qigong, I had no idea of what it could do. My only reference was a demo by Sifu, Michael Tse. However, that was enough for me to feel the energy emanating from him, his movement and personality. I knew then that there was something there, but that the only way to find out was to do it! As Sifu also explained in that demo, we should not think too much about the outcome or what to expect exactly, just practise and it will happen. And that was what I did. I went to classes and tried not to expect anything. To my surprise, class was very different. No harsh discipline. No pressure to do things that I did not want to do. My first feeling was just go to the class and enjoy being there, being with other people who are helpful and understanding. Also to give 100% to my practice since Sifu was giving more than 100% to the class and to me.

Personally, although I used to do other martial arts and exercises, I always felt there was something missing (i.e. internal training). So I was always slightly ill, having flu, being run down, injured and generally not feeling good and happy. The first thing I noticed was my general health getting much better and lots of symptoms which disappeared. Then the feeling of relaxation and being a person that I wanted to be, returned. From then on, everything got better for me in my life. Better health, friends, love and life.

I believe feeling simple and happy is very important in doing any type of exercise. Apart from the health advantages, which I could never have envisaged, the sense of happiness and simplicity were bonuses. In addition, I like belonging to a unique family of people who share Qigong and are willing to help others all over the world for a better life. This is what I have always looked for in life.

Shahriar Sepangi
London, England

Overcoming Curvature of the Spine

How has practising Wild Goose Qigong helped me? Well, it has in many ways. First of all, it has helped me to overcome what was considered to be a medical problem: a slight curvature of the base of the spine, which caused me pain in the hip area. Sue Burton, to whom I went for Chinese massage, advised me to take up Qigong, and I must say that it has solved the problem, at least for the time being, as I have had no symptom for three years.

In a more general way, my practice keeps me physically fit, strong and supple. I am now 64 years old and began Qigong when I was 60 years old. It is good for my posture, my breathing and my balance. So, naturally, I feel that it is also good for my mental and emotional energy. It increases my self-awareness and stability, makes me feel grounded and light at the same time. At another level, I appreciate the aesthetic side of it. I enjoy seeing all those bodies, of all shapes and sizes, moving - or learning to move - in such a graceful and harmonious way.

Marie Ball
Wimbledon, England

Natural Flow

I started learning Wild Goose Qigong about a year and a half ago. I definitely notice its effects when I manage to get into a good routine of practising. Not having a garden or other suitable space, I often can't manage to practise as consistently as I'd like. Over last Christmas I went home to see my family and had both the leisure time and the room to get regular practice. With regular practice I began to feel more stable in terms of mood and generally more relaxed. One of the main things I noticed was highlighted by the millennium New Year's Eve. Despite getting only a few hours sleep, someone commented that I looked relatively fresh compared to other people who'd kept the same hours. I certainly felt better than I would have expected to. I find that it helps a lot with physical activities. I do a lot of cycling and Qigong helps recovery so that you don't get badly stiff muscles and joints. Being calmer seems to help a lot with sport as you tend not to expend energy wildly and you have more control over what you are doing. You are more aware of the way your body is working so things flow more naturally.

Peter Dickinson
England

Back Pain and Qigong

Several years ago, I had an accident that seriously affected my back. I completely ruptured one of the disks in my lower back. In addition, there was a stress fracture in the adjacent vertebrae. I went from being an active person to being like an old man. I was unable to even sit up for long periods of time. Western medicine gave me a small operation and confined me to bed for 6 months. When that did not work I was put into a body cast for 3 months, and after that I was given hydrotherapy. A final solution of fusing the two vertebrae together was offered to me.

Peter Walfisz performing "Look for Food"

However, after this, I was not prepared to let the Western doctors 'mess around' any more, so I opted not to undergo the operation. Instead, I decided to investigate alternative medicines and started to read books on self healing. I went to see an acupuncturist, and after a few sessions my back was a bit better. I was now able to sit upright for extended periods, which was more then I had been able to do for months. The acupuncturist then suggested I take up Taiji.

After some research, I discovered Michael Tse and Wild Goose Qigong. I went to a class and was told by him that, if I did the class for three months, I would see real results. I asked if I needed to see him for private Qigong therapy. I was absolutely desperate and would have paid a lot of money to someone if they could help to heal my back. Michael Tse told me that I need only attend the classes. If he were a person of lower moral character he could have easily taken advantage of me! He did not, and I now lead a very active life and am able to touch my toes, do martial arts, and basically everything else that Western medicine told me that I would not be able to do.

I have now been studying Qigong for over six years and have noticed many additional benefits. I am very healthy, rarely get sick, and am definitely happier and more balanced. I would recommend Wild Goose Qigong to anyone wishing to improve their health and life. I would also like to thank my Sifu, Michael Tse and the Tse Qigong Centre for their quality of instruction and for introducing me to Wild Goose Qigong.

> Yours faithfully,
> Peter Walfisz
> London, England

What My Body Needs

Through learning Wild Goose Qigong I'm now aware that my body constantly tells me what its needs are and by addressing these needs I can keep healthy. This awareness continues to shape the way I live, influencing how I chose to work and socialise. It's an interesting journey!

> Caroline Garvey
> Stockport, England

Comforting Stillness

While learning, a strange unnaturalness accompanies the unfamiliar movements. As you become more familiar with them, they in turn allow you to become more aware of your own body, how you use it and where the tension is. Daily practice gives a warm relaxation and a comforting stillness, in spite of the fullness of living. There is a strength to be had from the knowledge that these feelings return should the business of life overtake you, like it sometimes does!

> Martin Rooney
> Macclesfield, England

Increased Flexibility

I began Qigong in an attempt to mitigate the effects of osteo-arthritis and to improve my general health.. The exercises have increased my flexibility and given me a sense of wellbeing. I am more at ease and my life has become more balanced. As I continue to study Qigong my life becomes further enhanced.

> Terry Dudley
> Manchester, England

Health is the Most Important Thing

When I started studying Dayan Qigong I did not think I was particularly unhealthy. In fact I only really started as I wanted to find out what it was all about. Back then I was more interested in martial arts, being 20 years old, but when I listened to others talking to Sifu about the exercises and Qi and how it had helped them, I grew curious.

As I began to study and the Qi was stimulated in my body, I started to notice tingling sensations and discovered aches and pains I never knew I had. The aches seemed to move around, mainly in my spine, but in a strange way they felt quite positive. Now I do not suffer from any aches or pains, apart from the odd pulled muscle now and again and am much more flexible. Now a few years have passed, I still suffer the odd cold or bout of flu, but I can always shake these problems off very quickly and I have not needed to see a doctor (of any kind) for more than ten years.

Dayan Qigong has given me a box full of tools with which I am able to maintain and repair my body, mind and energy. It has helped me in many ways, not only on a physical level. In fact it has changed my entire life. I cannot imagine being without it as it has helped me become who I am today. Sifu always says, whatever happens, your health is the most important thing. Without it, you cannot do what you want in life. Dayan Qigong gives you this and much more.

Darryl Moy
Manchester, England

Calm State of Mind

Practising Qigong regularly has resulted for me in benefits to body, mind and spirit. Physically the effects have been an easeful body, with little or no illness. Whenever the hint of a cold begins to materialise, it never develops fully and soon passes away. If a muscle is pulled or there is a bruise, it soon heals. Similarly, if there is a burn or scald, the initial pain soon passes and the injury heals quickly. Mentally I find concentration easier than before and find that practising slows my mind down, putting me in a more relaxed, calm state of mind. Qigong has enriched me spiritually by becoming aware of the philosophy behind the practice; becoming aware of the lessons in nature, the interplay of yin and yang and the five elements. I can honestly say that my life has been immeasurably enriched through the practice of Qigong, and I thank Michael Tse and all his teachers for what I have learned.

John Spinetto, Sheffield, England

Closer to Nature

Wild Goose has helped me be calmer and not lose my temper so easily. I feel more flexible in body and mind. I have more energy, better strength and a more balanced view of life. It brings me closer to nature and the energy of the universe.

Vicky McCurdy
Manchester, England

Improved Sleeping

Wild Goose has helped me to take time out from my hectic schedule, to spend time with my wife doing something together, which has helped me to bind more deeply with her. On a physical level it has helped me be a calmer person and has undoubtedly improved my sleeping pattern.

Cleve McCurdy
Manchester, England

"Skim over the Sea"

Natural Balance

Wild Goose Qigong keeps me fit enough to live my life to the full and cope with the inevitable changes of getting older. It has helped my back recover, when I pulled it after an excessive bout of gardening, without resorting to medication. I prefer the natural balance of Wild Goose Qigong to any other exercise or discipline.

Sylvia Royle
Middleton, England

Body and Life Balance

I began to study Wild Goose Qigong over seven years ago. I initially went to class looking for something that would ease the awful stress I was under at work and help the headaches and neck pain that had become increasingly worse. It had gotten to the point where I experienced a headache at least once a week if not more and there were many times that I could barely move my head to look over my shoulder. Being only twenty-nine years old, I felt that there had to be a change or else it could affect my future.

It took me a long while to finally decide to go to class, partly because I had never heard of Qigong and had never been a person to attend classes. I also felt very shy to go along to a group of strangers and try to learn movement, for which I am very clumsy and slow to pick up. Finally, though, my health began to deteriorate further and I felt it was now or never. I can still remember my first lesson vividly. Sifu was away and his senior student, John Hayes taught me. Although I felt quite dumb, he was very friendly and took a lot of time and patience to make me feel comfortable and he went through the movements until I could remember on my own. I decided to go back the next week and then the next. It was not long, within a month, that I began to notice that I felt more relaxed and that my cold hands began to actually have heat in them during meditation.

Jessica Blackwell helping a fellow student

As the months went on, I read more about the exercises and background of the skill and came to be fascinated by its long history. I knew that somehow, by some stroke of fate, I was studying a very profound art. In the beginning, I found it difficult even to touch my toes and would lose balance easily, but slowly I found my balance getting better as I finished the 1st 64 movements of the Wild Goose Qigong and moved onto the 2nd 64 movements. I rarely had headaches and I slept much better. On a visit home to see my parents who had not seen me in a year, I was told that I was more patient and kind. Qigong had not only made me more healthy, it had made me nicer to be around.

I left my job a few years after beginning my studies. Somehow chasing after money did not seem so important any more. To me the most important thing was my health, and if I had enough money for living expenses and study, then I was satisfied. I still have a long way to go and am still learning with every step, but for me, Wild Goose Qigong and the Kunlun Dayan System is a life journey, one which has brought me to myself and given me a purpose. I am fortunate indeed to have met such a teacher as Tse Sifu who has been able to keep this skill pure and share with us all how to respect the Chinese culture and skill.

Jessica Blackwell
Manchester, England

Helps Visual Impairment

When I was ten years old, I had an operation for a brain tumour, the result of which left me with a visual impairment and a damaged sense of balance. My body's way of dealing with the loss of balance and vision was to stiffen my body to hold myself up. As a result, my hips and shoulders became less mobile which led to me waddling when I walked. My posture became worse because I went everywhere peering down at the ground with a bent back and neck.

Twenty years on and I was unaware of my posture and how I moved until a friend of my brother asked him why I walked like an old man, looking down at the ground all the time! Also, it was around this time that I started to get periods of numbness in my hands and tingling in my neck. So I decided to do something about it. I left my home in the Isle of Man and went to live in Manchester so that I could study Qigong with my Sifu, Michael Tse.

Since beginning Qigong with Sifu, my past posture has changed, my balance has improved because of learning to sink and relax with Qigong movements. This has really improved the way I move

Martin Gale - improved balance and flexibility

about. I no longer walk like an old man and because of these things, my health has changed. This is due to the fact that my Qi can flow and my lungs are open. When I began Qigong, my expectations of my own abilities to progress were low, but with the guidance and diligent teaching from Sifu, I have progressed step by step. It has been hard work but worth it. When in 2000 I was invited to attend the Wild Goose Instructor course, I was amazed at my own progress, to the point where I received a certificate authorising me to teach the 1st 64 movements of Wild Goose Qigong.

Four years ago, when I started Qigong, I could never have expected how much my life could change and how much I could learn with the introduction of Wild Goose Qigong and the Tse Qigong Centre in my life. Thank you, Sifu, and the Tse Qigong Centre.

Martin Gale
Manchester, England

Qigong Warm Up

I initially began to study Wild Goose Qigong thinking that it would make a good warm up for my Chen Taijiquan practice, but now I have to say it takes centre stage over my Taijiquan practice. Once I started going to my weekly classes, I found it very enjoyable and almost a light relief from the hard work of Taijiquan. Every week I was shown some new moves and practised them over and over, adding to what I had learned. Soon I had completed the 1st 64 movements of Wild Goose Qigong and soon enough began to learn the 2nd 64 movements. I soon found that the urgency which I had to complete the first set of movements backed off with the second set and I was quite happy to take longer learning the new moves and going over them. I always felt good and accomplished on my way home from class, even those weeks when I had not learned anything new but just gone over and over previous moves.

It is now over four years since I began to learn the Wild Goose Qigong system and I am still practising and polishing my form. I have found that the set of Balancing Gong exercises now learned as the introduction for the Wild Goose form has become my Qigong foundation which I practise daily. I am thirty-five years old and I am more flexible than I can ever remember being. I am also more aware of my body and how I treat it. I think I am probably more relaxed and easier going as a person.

I have a new set of people at home through my regular classes with Sifu Julian Wilde, and also by attending some residential courses with my Sigong, Michael Tse. The residential courses were great. Even though I had already completed the Wild Goose form, I learned so much by spending time going through every movement and principle in detail that my Qigong practice really took a lift from it, in addition to having so much fun. Even though there were so many different characters from a variety of places and different walks of life, we all had a common interest...Wild Goose Qigong.

Qigong has also helped me through life's ups and downs. Dayan Qigong has simply become a part of my life and I believe it will remain so. There is just so much depth to it and always something new to learn. My ongoing thanks to my Sifu, Julian Wilde, in Norwich and of course to Sigong Michael Tse and to all at the Tse Qigong Centre. May the goose continue to spread its wings!

John Telling,
Norwich, England

Recovering From Open Heart Surgery

On June 19, 1997 I underwent surgery to repair an ascending aortic aneurysm, which had over a six month period reached a near critical stage. The surgical procedure involved splitting the breastbone and spreading apart my chest cavity. I had been going downhill healthwise for six months. My pulse rate would be up to 157 when I woke up in the morning and I was not sleeping well. Dr. Woo, my cardiologist said that he was astounded that I was still here because the condition had gotten so bad. After the surgery I was on a number of drugs for blood pressure, pulse rate and blood thinning. One of the prescriptions was Digitalis which poisoned me, causing me to be out of it for two days. I left the hospital on June 30, 1997 and returned home.

At home with good food, Chinese herbal remedies and acupuncture I began to recover, although I did not have any real zest for life and was only getting snatches of sleep in a recliner chair which was the only place I could relax comfortably. My Sifu had been encouraging me to do as many of the Taiji Qigong exercises as I could manage, without overdoing it. Sometime near the end of November I decided to stop taking prescription drugs as I felt they were responsible for some of the problems I was having - fluid retention in my extremities, unsteady balance, lassitude and so on.

In the spring of 1998 I decided to do more Qigong and began doing Dayan Qigong again in earnest. I found that my breathing rhythm was way off and I had forgotten some of the movements. Sifu got me going again and gradually things became easier and I kept remembering the things Sigong had said when instructing us, "relax the body, forget everything, breathe naturally, keep your back straight and so on". It wasn't until later in that spring that I really felt like living again and learned Swimming Dragon Qigong. So there is still hope for me. Thanks to Qigong, my healing and development continue.

John Hayes - 'Recover Qi'.

> Brian Cole
> Canada

The Story So Far

I discovered Qigong quite by chance, through my martial art studies, meeting both Michael Tse and Ip Chun for the first time and on the same day in 1987. It was in fact a Wing Chun seminar and Ip Sigong had invited Michael Tse on to the floor to explain the concept of Qi. Instead of an explanation, Michael gave a demonstration which fascinated me and left me wanting to explore further a subject previously hidden to me and most of the western world. Qigong, a Chinese skill of great antiquity, was in its infancy in the West.

At that stage I had spent fifteen years studying Karate and had picked up a few injuries which were not improving with age. The nature of my training was contributing to a slow deterioration in the injuries that would eventually mean that I would have to stop. Reluctant to give up I was now running my new-found interest in Qigong alongside my Karate training, believing I had the answer to balancing the physical excesses of one against the healing potential of the other.

Gradually, with time, Qigong took over and became part of my life and part of my daily routine. The injuries healed and my interest grew, not only in its healing potential but the philosophy and culture from which it had developed. After twelve years of study, it continues to be an absorbing subject which can be approached on many levels physically and intellectually. Therein lies the secret of its longevity. That magic word, balance!!

It is difficult to sum up the benefits without sounding like an evangelist. My personal poem derived from my studies reflects my Daoist tendencies.

When you go too far one way and things are difficult

> Let go,
> Take it easy
> Follow your heart
> Rediscover your nature.
> Do nothing by doing something-
> Qigong

John Hayes
New Malden, England

Stronger and More Flexible

My experiences of practising Wild Goose for several years are always expanding. I am still learning and discovering new things in the practice. The polishing courses were also very valuable, and I realized that there is so much more to it than I ever imagined. It appears the process of discovering and learning within the movements is endless. The benefits reaped from the practice are far reaching on many levels, and the resulting health and well-being are very uplifting.

Some of the changes I have noticed in myself are that my body has become stronger and more flexible, stiffness goes and aches and pains move out. I feel the Qigong unblocks the places that feel blocked. I used to have a lot of trouble with my knees, and now they are strong again. My circulation has improved and I feel warmer. My eyesight always improves after I practise, and I move with less effort and greater direction. My mind becomes more focused and I feel more intuitive. If I practise outside, the benefits feel stronger, and I feel closer to nature and more connected to the earth, and generally my awareness increases. I also found that over time my body shape changed, from being too thin to becoming sturdier and stronger and balanced. Wild Goose Qigong occupies a very special place in my life, and I feel extremely lucky to have found this practice, and to be able to learn from such a dedicated and genuine teacher, Michael Tse. Thank you.

Best Regards

Sue Laing

London, England

Qigong Helps Chronic Illness

I began practising Wild Goose Qigong with Sifu Michael Tse around seven years ago. I had heard about Wild Goose Qigong health benefits and having suffered chronic illness and at times acute pain I decided to give it a try. After about six months of regular practice, my condition began to improve. I continued to practise and attend classes for about two years, by which time my previous symptoms were almost unnoticeable.

The Wild Goose system takes time and patience to learn but the school in Manchester which I attend has a relaxed and friendly atmosphere. You can witness a range of different skills being practised from beginners to seniors and Sifu Michael Tse himself demonstrating from time to time.

Howard Dutton

St Helens, England

Appendix A

Chinese and English Names of Movements

Chinese and English Names of Movements

Wild Goose Qigong 1st 64

1.	Starting Position	起式
2.	Spread Wings	展翅
3.	Close Wings	合翅
4.	Draw Wings to the Back	折窝
5.	Flick Wings	抖膀
6.	Draw Wings to the Back	折窝
7.	Flick Wings	抖膀
8.	Lift Up	上举

9.	Twine Fingers	合掌
10.	Turn Palms Up	翻掌
11.	Bend Waist	下腰
12.	Twine Hands	纏手
13.	Recover Qi	回氣
14.	Twist Left Toes	左弹足
15.	Push Qi	推氣
16.	Scoop Qi	撈氣
17.	Turn Body and Recover Qi	轉身回氣
18.	Twist Right Toes	右弹足
19.	Pull Qi	推氣
20.	Scoop Qi	撈氣
21.	Twine Hands	纏手
22.	Cloud Hands	雲手
23.	Brush Waist	涮腰
24.	Drop Arms & Recover Qi	落臂回氣

25.	Spread Single Wing	单展翅
26.	Step Forward & Extend the Wing	上步伸膀
27.	Wind Hand Around Head and Ears	缠手过耳
28.	Press Qi Down	下压
29.	Prop Up Qi	上托
30.	Recover Qi	回气
31.	Scoop the Moon	捞月
32.	Turn Body	转身
33.	Step Forward & Look at Palm	上步望掌
34.	Look at the Moon	望月
35.	Press Qi	压气
36.	Turn Body & Press Qi	转身压气
37.	Swim Forward	泳劲
38.	Look Down at Water	瞅水
39.	Pat Water & Fly Away	拍水飞翔
40.	Drink Water	饮水

41.	Gaze at the Sky	望天
42.	Recover Qi	歸氣
43.	Grasp Qi	抓氣
44.	Turn Palm Up and Gather Qi	翻亭摟氣
45.	Hold the Ball	抱球
46.	Rotate the Qi Ball	搽球
47.	Turn the Body and Rotate Qi the Ball	轉身搽球
48.	Hold Qi	抱氣
49.	Pour Qi	罡氣
50.	Raise Wings	抬膀
51.	Drop Wings	翻翅
52.	Bring Wings to the Back	背翅
53.	Fly Up to the Side	起扇上飛
54.	Turn Body	轉身
55.	Fly Upward	飛上
56.	Skim over the Sea	過九飛翔

57.	Turn Body	轉身
58.	Fly Upward	飛上
59.	Look for Food	尋食
60.	Turn Body	轉身
61.	Look for the Nest	尋高
62.	Turn Body and Swim	轉身泳動
63.	Sleep Peacefully and Recover Qi	安睡歸氣
64.	Shou Gong	收式

Diagrams of Commonly Used Acupoints

Acupoints on the Front of the Body

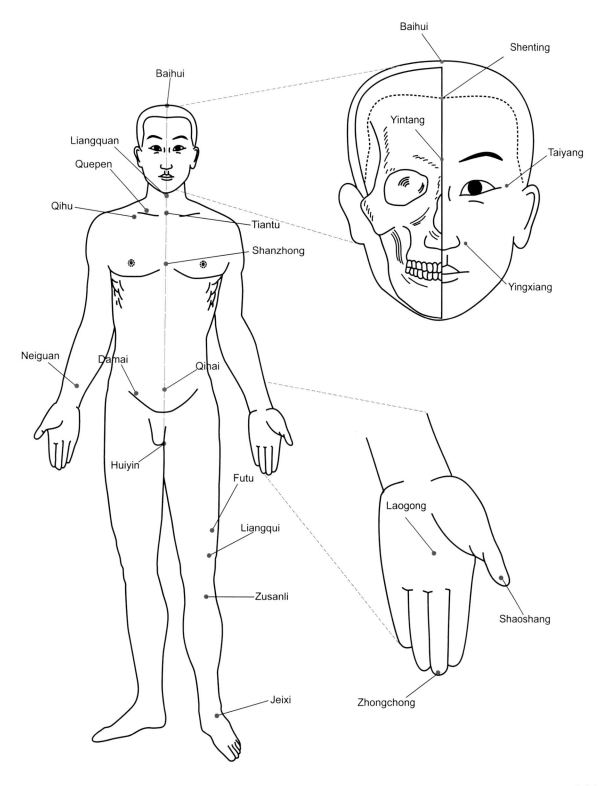

Acupoints on the Back of the Body

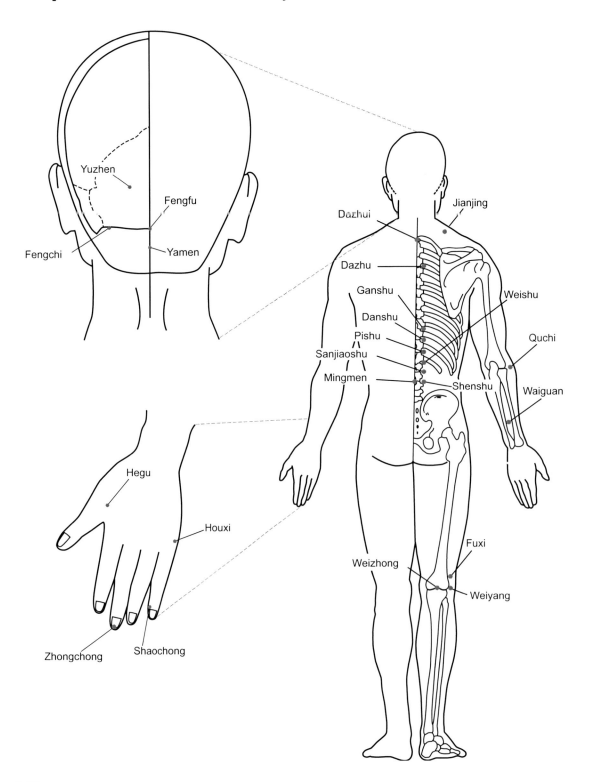

Yuzhen

Fengfu

Fengchi

Yamen

Dazhui

Jianjing

Dazhu

Ganshu

Weishu

Danshu

Pishu

Quchi

Sanjiaoshu

Mingmen

Shenshu

Waiguan

Hegu

Houxi

Fuxi

Weizhong

Weiyang

Zhongchong

Shaochong

Acupoints on the Side of the Body

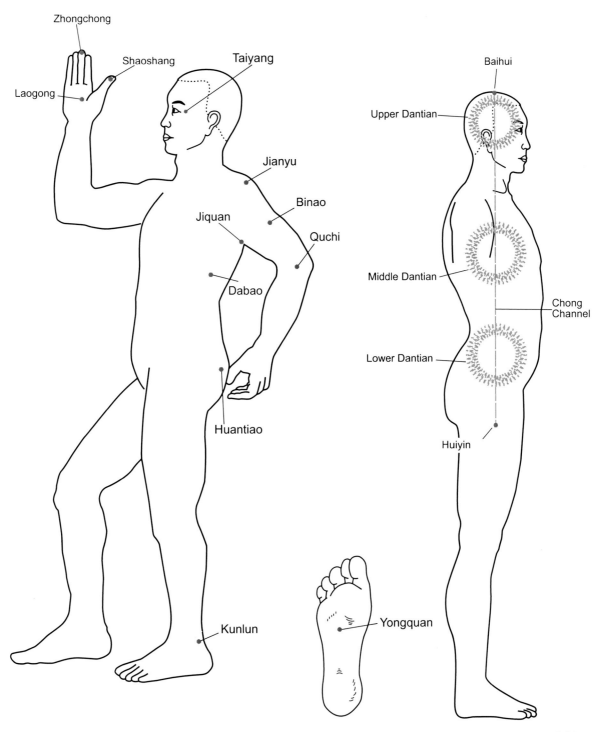

Zhongchong

Shaoshang

Taiyang

Laogong

Jianyu

Binao

Jiquan

Quchi

Dabao

Huantiao

Kunlun

Baihui

Upper Dantian

Middle Dantian

Chong Channel

Lower Dantian

Huiyin

Yongquan

Acupuncture Points Chinese Names and Meanings

Commonly Used Qigong Acupoints

Pronunciation of Acupoint		Chinese Character	Meaning	Benefit	Channel
Mandarin	Cantonese				
Baihui	Baat Wui	百會	Place of one hundred convergences	Can be used to treat shock, collapse, dizziness, headache and to help bring Qi to Triple Warmer.	Du
Binao	Bei Lau	臂臑	Outside of Upper Arm	Good for pain in the shoulder and arm, disease of the eye and blockages in the lymph glands.	Large Intestine Hand
Dabao	Dai Bau	大包	General Control	This point can be used to treat aching in the whole body as well as pain in the chest.	Spleen Foot
Daimai	Daai Mok	帶脈	Belt Channel	This point can help regulate blood flow in channels, lower back pain, relieve stomach ache, menstrual pain, cystitis.	Gall Bladder Foot
Danshu	Daan Yu	膽俞	Gall Bladder Shu	Good to help pain in head and back and numbness in the limbs as well as arthritis.	Urinary Bladder Foot

Commonly Used Qigong Acupoints

Pronunciation of Acupoint		Chinese Character	Meaning	Benefit	Channel
Mandarin	Cantonese				
Dazhu	*Dai Chu*	大杼	Top of the Back Bone Point	This point can help pain in the head and back, sore throat and numbness of limbs.	Urinary Bladder Foot
Dazhui	*Dai Zhoi*	大椎	Big Vertebrae	Can help cough, pain in shoulder and chest, relieve fever and sore throat.	Du
Fengchi	*Fong Chi*	風池	Wind Pond	This point is good for treating stiff neck, headache, ringing ears and deafness, insomnia, and redness in the eyes.	Gall Bladder Foot
Fengfu	*Fong Fu*	風府	Windy Mansion	Can be used to relieve stiff neck, pain and swelling in the throat relating to the common cold. Also good for helping relieve migraines	Du
Futu	*Fuhk Tou*	伏兔	Prostrate Rabbit	Can help paralysis and numbness of lower limbs.	Stomach Foot

Commonly Used Qigong Acupoints

Pronunciation of Acupoint		Chinese Character	Meaning	Benefit	Channel
Mandarin	Cantonese				
Fuxi	Fou Keuk	浮郄	Shallow Gap	This point is good for paralysis of lower limbs, relieving cystitis, constipation and insomnia.	Urinary Bladder Foot
Ganshu	Gaan Yu	肝俞	Liver Shu	This point can help jaundice, abdomen pain, blurred vision and night blindness.	Urinary Bladder Foot
Hegu	Hap Guk	合谷	Connected Valley	Good for headache, toothache, pain in the eyes, sore throat and facial paralysis. Can help promote blood and Qi circulation.	Large Intestine Hand
Houxi	Hou Chi	後谿	Back Stream	This point is good for night sweating, pain and stiffness in neck, red eye, deafness and ringing in the ears.	Small Intestine Hand

Commonly Used Qigong Acupoints

Pronunciation of Acupoint		Chinese Character	Meaning	Benefit	Channel
Mandarin	Cantonese				
Huantiao	Waan Tiu	環跳	Circular Jump	Good for hip pain, weakness or numbness in the lower body. It can help back pain and help strengthen the legs.	Gall Bladder Foot
Huiyin	Wui Yum	會陰	Converging Yin	This point can help irregular menstruation, prolapse of uterus, haemorrhoids, constipation and mental disorder.	Ren
Jianjing	Gin Jang	肩井	Shoulder Well	This point can help vertigo, stiff neck and shoulder and back pain.	Gall Bladder Foot
Jianliao	Gin Maau	肩髎	Shoulder Crevice	This point is good for aching pain, spasm, and weakness of shoulder and also weakness in the arm.	Sanjiao (Triple Warmer) Hand

Commonly Used Qigong Acupoints

Pronunciation of Acupoint		Chinese Character	Meaning	Benefit	Channel
Mandarin	Cantonese				
Jianyu	Gin Yu	肩髃	Shoulder Blade	This point can help rheumatism in the shoulder, fever, weakness in the arm and frozen shoulder.	Large Intestine Hand
Jiexi	Gai Kai	解谿	Cleaning the Stream	Can help stomach Qi flow properly, clear heat and relieve edema. It can also help swelling and pain of the ankle.	Stomach Foot
Jingmen	Ging Mun	京門	Capital Gate	Good for lower back pain, diarrhoea and abdominal pain.	Gall Bladder Foot
Jiquan	Gik Chun	極泉	Origin of the Spring	This point can help pain in the elbow and arm, depression. It can also help pain in the heart region.	Heart Hand
Kunlun	Kwun Laan	昆侖	Big Mountain	Good for headache, waist and back pain.	Urinary Bladder Foot

Commonly Used Qigong Acupoints

Pronunciation of Acupoint		Chinese Character	Meaning	Benefit	Channel
Mandarin	Cantonese				
Laogong	Lao Gong	勞宮	Laboured Place	This point is good for poor appetite, epilepsy, heart pain and foul breath. It can calm someone who is having hysterics.	Pericardium Hand
Liangqui	Leung Yauh	梁丘	Hill Ridge	Can help gastric pain, lower back pain and swelling of knee and breast.	Stomach Foot
Lianquan	Lim Cheun	廉泉	Tongue Spring	This point can help with stiffness of the tongue, hoarse voice and blisters in the mouth.	Ren
Lower Dantian	Hah Daan Tihn	下丹田	'Dan' means Crystal. 'Tian' means Field.	This area relates to the kidneys and stores Jing Qi.	(An area not a channel)
Middle Dantian	Zhong Daan	中丹田	'Dan' means Crystal. 'Tian' means Field.	This area relates to the heart and stores pure Qi.	(An area not a channel)

Commonly Used Qigong Acupoints

Pronunciation of Acupoint		Chinese Character	Meaning	Benefit	Channel
Mandarin	Cantonese				
Mingmen	Ming Mun	命門	Gate of Life	This point is good for kidneys, low energy and backache. It is also good for impotence and seminal emission and strengthening the uterus.	Du
Neiguan	Loi Kwan	內關	Inner Pass	Good for heart and stomach pain, migraines, hand problems, sore throat and for treating shock. It can also help treat nervousness and mental disorders.	Pericardium Hand
Pishu	Pei Yu	脾俞	Spleen Shu	Can help jaundice, diarrhoea, dysentery, weakness of limbs and vomiting.	Urinary Bladder

Commonly Used Qigong Acupoints

Pronunciation of Acupoint		Chinese Character	Meaning	Benefit	Channel
Mandarin	Cantonese				
Qihai	Hei Hoi	氣海	Energy Sea	This point relates to the Lower Dantian, kidneys, sexual organs and urinary bladder. Good for Qi and blood circulation and to regulate menstruation.	Ren
Qihu	Hei Wu	氣户	Energy Gate	Good for asthma, bronchitis, cough and pain in the chest. Relates to the lungs	Stomach Foot
Quchi	Kuk Chi	曲池	Bent Pond	This point can help pain in the eye, toothache, pain in arm joints and high fever.	Large Intestine Hand
Quepen	Kut Pun	缺盆	Broken Plate	Good for breathing problems and coughing. It can help with neck pain, numbness in arms and shoulder pain.	Stomach Foot

Commonly Used Qigong Acupoints

Pronunciation of Acupoint		Chinese Character	Meaning	Benefit	Channel
Mandarin	Cantonese				
Sanjiao-shu	Sam Tzi Yu	三焦俞	Triple Warmer Shu	Can help headache, vertigo, dysentery, jaundice and lower pack pain.	Urinary Bladder
Shan-zhong	Taan Jong	膻中	Middle Altar	This point relates to the Middle Dantian and the heart. It can help heart and chest pain as well as asthma and cough.	Ren
Shao-chong	Siu Chung	少衝	Little Rush	This point is good for treating pain in the chest, sore throat and high fever.	Heart Hand
Shao-shang	Siu Seung	少商	Young Shang	Good for sore throat, fever, mental disorders and any pain in the fingers.	Lung Hand
Shenshu	San Yu	腎俞	Kidney Shu	This point is good for the kidneys, low energy, tiredness, stress, backache, ringing in the ears and menstrual problems.	Urinary Bladder

Commonly Used Qigong Acupoints

Pronunciation of Acupoint		Chinese Character	Meaning	Benefit	Channel
Mandarin	Cantonese				
Shenting	San Ting	神庭	Spiritual Courtyard	This point is good for headaches, vertigo, asthma, restlessness and convulsion.	Du
Taiyang	Tai Yeung	太陽	Large Yang	This is good for headaches, motion sickness, pain in the eye or decline in vision.	Extraordinary Point
Tiantu	Tin Dat	天突	Sky Prominence	This is important for breathing and helps to open the channels for Qi and is good for the lungs. Can help coughing and hoarseness.	Ren
Upper Dantian	Shang Daan Tihn	上丹田	'Dan' means Crystal. 'Tian' means Field.	The Upper Dantian is the area in the middle of the forehead above the eyebrows. It relates to the brain and intuition development.	(An area not a channel)

Commonly Used Qigong Acupoints

Pronunciation of Acupoint		Chinese Character	Meaning	Benefit	Channel
Mandarin	Cantonese				
Waiguan	Ngoi Kwan	外關	Outer Pass	This point is good for deafness, ringing in the ears, hand and shoulder problems and for helping ease constipation.	Sanjiao Hand
Weishu	Wai Yu	胃俞	Stomach Shu	Good for stomach pain, pain in chest, nausea and vomiting, diarrhoea with undigested food and dysentery.	Urinary Bladder Foot
Weiyang	Wai Yeung	委陽	Popiteal Yang	Can help full sensation in the chest and abdomen. Can also help treat constipation.	Urinary Bladder Foot
Weizhong	Wai Jung	委中	Popiteal Centre	Good for stiffness in the back and can help treat colic in the upper abdomen.	Urinary Bladder Foot
Yamen	Nga Mun	啞門	Mute Gate	Can help headache, stiff neck, muteness and deafness and chronic convulsion.	Du

Commonly Used Qigong Acupoints

Pronunciation of Acupoint		Chinese Character	Meaning	Benefit	Channel
Mandarin	Cantonese				
Yingxiang	Ying Hueng	迎香	Welcome the Fragrance	This point can help relieve sinus problems, facial paralysis, improve sense of smell and help swelling of the face.	Large Intestine Hand
Yintang	Yan Tong	印堂	Room for Using the Official Chop	Can help headache, vertigo, common cold, insomnia and pain in the forehead.	Extra-ordinary point
Yongquan	Yong Chuen	涌泉	Pouring Spring	This point is good for releasing negative energy and excess heat from the body.	Kidney Foot
Yuzhen	Yuk Tsum	玉枕	Jade Pillow	This point can help headache, pain in the eye, pain in the neck and blurring of vision.	Urinary Bladder Foot

Commonly Used Qigong Acupoints

Pronunciation of Acupoint		Chinese Character	Meaning	Benefit	Channel
Mandarin	Cantonese				
Zhong-chong	Jung Chung	中衝	Middle Rush	This point can help heart pain, headache, pain in elbow and loss of consciousness.	Pericardium Hand
Zusanli	Juk Sam Li	足三里	Foot Three Li (Mile)	This point can help mental disorders, vomiting, swelling of limbs and lower abdomen as well as general body weakness.	Stomach Foot

Key to Mandarin Pronunciation

Pinyin Sound	Pinyin Example Word	Pronunciation as per the exmple word
iang	xiang	(as in) shee-ong
zh	zhong	(as in) jong
ai	bai	(as in) buy
an	dan	(as in) con
ao	lao	(as in) bow
e	he	(as in) afflict
ei	nei	(as in) lay
en	men	(as in) run
eng	feng	(as in) rung
i	chi	(as in) bee
ian	tian	(as in) ee-in
ie	jie	(as in) measure
ing	ming	(as in) king
ong	gong	(as in) song
ou	hou	(as in) go
qu	quan	(as in) choo-ahn
q	qi	(as in) chee
u	fu	(as in) loo
uan	huan	(as in) oo-ahn
ui	hui	(as in) bouy
un	kun	(as in) soon
x	xi	(as in) she
xu	xu	(as in) shoo

Key to Cantonese Pronunciation

Cantonese Sound	Cantonese Example Word	Pronunciation as per the exmple word
ai	baai	(as in) buy
aan	waan	(as in) bon
aat	baat	(as in) yacht
ai	tai	(as in) high
an	yan	(as in) fun
ap	hap	(as in) cup
ei	hei	(as in) lay
eun	cheun	(as in)
eung	heung	(as in) earn
i	chi	(as in) bee
in	tin	(as in) seen
ing	ying	(as in) sing
iu	tiu	(as in) see you
ng	ngoi	(as in) sing
oi	loi	(as in) boy
ok	mok	(as in) sock
ong	fong	(as in) gong
ts	tsum	(as in) 'j'
u	yuk	(as in) book
u	yu	(as in) too

Authorised Tse Qigong Centre Instructors

Authorised
Tse Qigong Centre
Instructors

UK

Tse Qigong Centre
PO Box 59
Altrincham WA15 8FS
Tel 0845 838 2285
Tel 0161 929 4485
tse@qimagazine.com

www.tseqigongcentre.com
www.qimagazine.com

Michael Tse founded the Tse Qigong Centre in 1990 along with Qi Magazine. We now have instructors around the world who are authorised by the Tse Qigong Centre. Our instructors must have studied with the Centre at least three years before they can be nominated by their Sifu to take part in instructor training.

The foremost quality that we look for in a student is that they have a good heart. The next is a good foundation and love of the skill on which they can then later continue to develop and polish.

Our instructors continue to attend training courses to renew their certificates at least once every two or three years. This is to maintain the standard and high quality of the skill, like in a profession.

For a list of current, qualified Tse Qigong Centre instructors, please visit our website on www. tseqigongcentre.com or www.qimagazine.com or contact our office.

Further Reading
and Viewing

Wild Goose Qigong Books by Michael Tse

Wild Goose Qigong 2nd 64 Part 1

Filled with more stories of Grandmaster Yang Meijun and her student Michael Tse, revised exercise descriptions and principles and some Wild Goose Qigong knowledge never released before, like how the movements connect to the 64 gua of the Yijing. As the 2nd 64 is more complex and twice as long as the 1st 64 ths book covers the first half of the form.

Wild Goose Qigong 2nd 64 Part 2

The concluding part of the 2nd 64 Movements of Wild Goose Qigong by Master Michael Tse. Includes the remaining movements of the Wild Goose Qigong 2nd 64 form and chapters on the Five Heart Centre and how the Yijing and the Gau relate to the movement. With even more detail and knowledge this is the largest book of the series!

Wild Goose Qigong DVDs by Michael Tse

Wild Goose Qigong 1st 64 Part 1 - DVD

Wild Goose Qigong 1st 64 Part 2 - DVD

Wild Goose Qigong 1st 64 Part 3 - DVD

The eagerly awaited series on Wild Goose Qigong's First 64 by Master Michael Tse. There is a wealth of information in the Wild Goose Qigong movements and Master Tse demonstrates the form with grace and clarity. He also expands upon the philosophy and culture of this beautiful Qigong form. In each lesson, Master Tse repeats the movements three times then goes on to explain its principles and more about any acupuncture points, channels or special hand movements used. There are close ups, side and slow motion views that will help your understanding deepen. Filmed at the base of the lush slopes of Hawaii's Ko'olau Mountain range, Master Michael Tse shares his profound insight and understanding of this ancient Chinese skill.

Other Publications by Michael Tse

Qigong For Healing and Relaxation

Michael Tse introduces a new series of individual Qigong movements which target specific parts of the body for healing and relaxation. This fully illustrated book is suitable for people new to Qigong as well as more experienced students. These exercises which were created by Michael Tse in 1996 are excellent for healing particular problems in the body, like arthritis, IBS, dizziness, tennis elbow, etc.

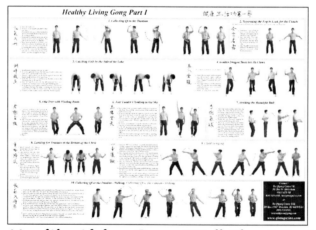

Healthy Living Gong Wall Chart Part 1

Charts are a great way to be able to learn a form or set of exercises as you do not need to keep referring back to a book each time you change to a new movement. This two- sided chart has both movement and descriptions on one side and a full set of all the main channels in the body as well as the acupoints used in Part I of Healthy Living Gong. The size of the chart is 841 x 594 mm, A1 (just over 33 inches by 23 inches).

Qi Journeys - Volume I

A selection of collected stories brings the reader to a better understanding of the Chinese internal arts and culture. Easy to read stories on Qigong, Life in general, Martial Arts, Feng Shui, Teacher/Student relationships as well as Philosophy. For anyone who likes a good story, particularly those interested in Chinese culture.

Qi Journeys - Volume II

Another selection of collected stories from Sifu Michael Tse covering many different aspects of Chinese culture, from Qigong, Martial Arts to Feng Shui. There is something for everyone. If you enjoyed Volume I, you will love Volume II.

Qigong DVDs

Healthy Living Gong Part I

This set of movements is for balancing and relaxing the body, working on such problems as insomnia, digestion, asthma, urinary tract problems, blood pressure, arthritis, dizziness, poor memory and too much worry, weak kidneys and stiff joints

Healthy Living Gong Part II

This second set of exercises develops overall fitness and coordination. This set of movements helps to make the body more flexible and will improve posture and make the legs and spine stronger. They can improve circulation, make the waist more flexible and hips stronger, develop stamina and help with weight loss.

Healthy Living Gong Part III

This third set of exercises is very interesting and will develop strength and power. Once you have learned the movements and practise them altogether without stopping, you will feel very warm and even sweating. This is the Yang side of Qigong movements whereas the movements in the first set are more gentle and Yin.

Balancing Gong

This DVD covers all eleven Balancing Gong exercises from Master Tse's book, Qigong for Health & Vitality. Michael Tse created Balancing Gong in 1993 to help his patients in his Qigong Healing practice. It is a series of gentle movements good for helping improve posture, relieve backache, arthritis, neck injury and knee problems as well as improving balance and coordination. These exercises are suitable for a variety of ages and levels of fitness.

Audio Tape

Meditate

In this audio tape, Master Tse introduces you to the concept of meditation and why it is vital to your wellbeing and then guides you through a meditation, helping you to relax and start to feel the benefits of quieting the body and mind.

Qi Magazine

Qi Magazine was founded by Michael Tse in 1990 as a way of bringing to the West authentic knowledge on Chinese skill and knowledge, such as Qigong, martial arts and Chinese medicine. He has expanded the magazine to include regular articles on Feng Shui, Buddhism, Daoism, Chinese horoscopes and philosophy.

For ordering
contact Tse Qigong Centre
or order on-line
www.tseqigongcentre.com
www.qimagazine.com

TSE
QIGONG CENTRE ®

氣功

Qigong